Praise for

NOT YOUR Mother's
POSTPARTUM BOOK

MW00633026

"A strikingly heartfelt resource for navigating the psychological complexities of motherhood, *Not Your Mother's Postpartum Book* is an unvarnished guide set out to help create a greater sense of comfort and ease throughout. By weaving their own stories among the latest research on maternal mental health, Caitlin and Chelsea have created a deeply illuminating book where mothers will feel seen and understood no matter the circumstances of their postpartum experience."

—**Jessica Zucker, PhD,** author of *I Had a Miscarriage:
A Memoir, a Movement*

"This empathetic and highly actionable book is exactly what every mom needs on her registry. The title says it all. It's the perfect companion guide for one of the most challenging times in a woman's life. I can't wait to gift it to every new mom I know."

—**Amanda White, LPC,** creator of @therapyforwomen,
author of *Not Drinking Tonight*

"Powerful! *Not Your Mother's Postpartum Book* is an informative book that every mother needs. It covers the topics no one talks about, despite the fact that they are nearly universal experiences for mothers. It's time we normalize the hard parts of motherhood. Caitlin and Chelsea bring this to us with thought-provoking reflection questions and exercises to help moms live more meaningfully during this both joyful and difficult season in life."

—**Tracy Dalgleish, PhD, CPsych,** author
of *I Didn't Sign Up for This*

"*Not Your Mother's Postpartum Book* is like the *What to Expect When You're Expecting* for postpartum moms. This book is easily digestible, entirely practical, and comes with skills and tools for everything from birth trauma to boundaries. This is a must-read for every new mom and mom-to-be."

—Morgan Van Epp Cutlip, PhD, relationships expert, @drmorgancutlip

"Mothering is hard. Mothers often feel unsupported and without a village. In writing this book, Caitlin and Chelsea have created a postpartum mental health workbook for new mothers to tap into therapeutic strategies from the comfort of their own homes. This is such a helpful and necessary resource. Their book is thoughtfully written and their words provide such containment for mothers navigating many common challenges, including pregnancy complications and loss, perinatal mood disorders, and returning to work. Chapters contain thought-provoking exercises alongside supportive affirmations and evidence-based information. This book is such a supportive read for any mother who is struggling with postpartum mental health or the challenges of motherhood."

—Kimberly Bennett, PsyD, founder of @the_psychologists_child

"*Not Your Mother's Postpartum Book* is the warm, validating, reassuring companion you need to navigate the chaos that is life after a baby. It's packed with helpful and normalizing information, as well as actionable skills that provide stability and a path forward to serve you in parenthood and beyond."

—Sunita Osborn, PsyD, author of *The Miscarriage Map* and *The Miscarriage Map Workbook*

Normalizing Post-Baby Mental Health Struggles,
Navigating #MOMLife, and Finding Strength Amid the Chaos

NOT YOUR
Mother's
POSTPARTUM
BOOK

CAITLIN SLAVENS, BAACS, MC, RPsych
CHELSEA BODIE, BSc, MACP, RPsych
@mamapsychologists

Published by
PESI Publishing, Inc.
3839 White Ave
Eau Claire, WI 54703

Cover: Amy Rubenzer
Editing: Jenessa Jackson, PhD
Layout: Amy Rubenzer and Alissa Schneider

ISBN: 9781683735823 (print)
ISBN: 9781683735830 (ePUB)
ISBN: 9781683735847 (ePDF)

PESI Publishing
pesipublishing.com

About the Authors

Caitlin Slavens, BAACS, MC, RPsych, is a registered psychologist, trained eye movement desensitization reprocessing (EMDR) therapist, and a certified Theraplay professional. She has additional training in attachment parenting, play therapy, child-adolescent mental health, and trauma modalities. Caitlin has two little ones who keep her constantly on the go (with a large cup of coffee in her hand).

Chelsea Bodie, BSc, MACP, RPsych, is a registered psychologist and certified perinatal mental health professional (PMH-C) with training in perinatal mood disorders, birth trauma, perinatal grief and loss, and infertility. She also has training in play therapy and child-adolescent mental health. Chelsea is a mom of two little ones who also keep her busy as they get into mischief on the farm.

For tips on parenting and all things postpartum, follow Caitlin and Chelsea on Instagram @mamapsychologists.

Acknowledgments

Where to start with acknowledgments, oh my goodness! When PESI Publishing first approached us to write this book, we were just two moms who were overwhelmed and struggling due to our experiences with the postpartum period, birth trauma, and the NICU. Now here we are with an online community of over 278,000 members and a published book.

First and foremost, we really want to thank our partners, Trevor and Colten, who have gone through this crazy journey with us. They encouraged us, inspired us, and provided us with many of the real-life examples we use in this book.

We would also like to thank our families, who came up with ideas for this book and who helped us edit it along the way. They believed in us, even when we didn't, and we wouldn't have made it this far in life without them. We especially want to thank our mothers, Jennifer and Marlene, who showed us what strength in motherhood looks like and who are also wonderful grandmothers to our own children.

Caitlin also wants to thank her Grandma Alice, whom she lost while in the final stages of writing this book: *You showed me the definition of unconditional love. I love you and miss you.*

Through the years, we have had many mentors, teachers, and colleagues who helped us become who we are. You know who you all are, and we cannot thank you enough.

We'd also like to thank our wonderful editors, Jenessa Jackson and Karsyn Morse, for encouraging us and keeping us on track.

Lastly, we would like to acknowledge the littles who made us moms! To our kids, Jaysik, Aubree, Blair, and Alix: You are the driving force behind what we do.

Contents

Introduction. xix

1 | Birth Trauma 1

What Is Birth Trauma? 1

Your Birth Experience. 5

But I Had a "Typical" Birth—Why Do I Feel This Way? 7

Can I Prevent It?. 8

What Can I Do?. 14

What About My Partner? 23

Takeaways. 24

2 | Body Image 27

What Is Body Image? 27

Common Postpartum Body Struggles. 30

Pelvic Floor Health Is Important Too 35

How to Cope with Body Image Struggles 36

Takeaways 45

3 | Boundaries. 47

What Are Boundaries? 47

Types of Boundaries 50

Why Is Setting Boundaries So Tough? 54

What Do Boundary Violations Look Like?. 54

Boundary Violations and the New Mom 57

How to Set a Boundary 58

Setting Boundaries in Different Areas of Your Life 62

What If Others Don't Respect My Boundary?. 69

Takeaways. 71

4 | **Breastfeeding, Formula Feeding & More** **73**

Forms of Feeding 74

Our Feeding Experiences 76

Your Feeding Journey 79

Dysphoric Milk Ejection Reflex vs. Breastfeeding Aversion. 82

Feeding and Mental Health 83

Takeaways. 94

5 | **The Contradiction of Motherhood** **97**

Parenting Attitudes. 99

Our Experiences with Contradiction 100

Your Experience with Contradiction. 102

Coping with the Contradiction 104

Takeaways. 113

6 | **Intrusive Thoughts** **115**

Categories of Intrusive Thoughts 116

Why Am I Having These Thoughts?. 118

Why Are These Thoughts Not Talked About?. 120

Managing Intrusive Thoughts. 122

Takeaways. 127

7 | Mental Load of Motherhood 129

How Does the Mental Load Develop? 129

The Default Parent 130

The Invisible Loads 132

How to Offset Some of the Load 135

Managing It All When It Feels So Unmanageable 138

Takeaways 144

8 | Mom Burnout 147

What Is Burnout? 148

What Fuels Burnout? 150

Sensory Overload in Parenting 152

Remedies for Burnout 155

Additional Remedies for Burnout 159

Takeaways 169

9 | Mom Guilt 171

Mother Blame 171

Shame vs. Guilt 174

What Triggers Us into Shame Mode? 176

Managing Shame in the Body 183

Managing Shame Thoughts 189

Shame Resilience 191

Takeaways 194

10 | Mother Wound **197**

The Mother Wound Today. 197

What the Mother Wound Looks Like. 199

People Pleasing and the Mother Wound 201

Healing the Mother Wound 203

Takeaways. 207

11 | Where Did I Go? Finding Yourself After Baby 209

The Maternal Identity Shift 210

The Push and Pull of Motherhood 211

The Myths of Motherhood. 212

Rediscovering Yourself 216

The Value Shift. 219

Takeaways. 221

12 | NICU/Preemie Moms **223**

Definitions 225

Statistics 227

Managing Guilt and Shame 227

Survival Tips for Navigating the NICU 234

Ways to Bond in the NICU 237

Caring for Other Children at Home. 240

Preparing to Return Home. 242

How to Support Someone in the NICU 244

Preparing for Subsequent Pregnancies. 246

Takeaways 247

13 | Other Types of Mamas & Families 251

Stories from Different Families 252

Our Family Structures Look Different 253

Finding the Support You Need 263

Takeaways 264

14 | Pregnancy Complications & Loss 267

What Is Infertility? 268

Complications in Pregnancy 272

Miscarriage and Pregnancy Loss 274

How the Medical Community Defines Miscarriage and Loss 276

Trying to Conceive After Pregnancy Loss 278

Defining Grief 282

Ways to Support a Grieving Mama 285

Takeaways 286

15 | Baby Blues & Perinatal Mood Disorders 289

Baby Blues 290

Postpartum Depression 298

Postpartum Anxiety 302

Postpartum Obsessive-Compulsive Disorder 305

Postpartum Posttraumatic Stress Disorder 308

Postpartum Rage 310

Postpartum Psychosis 314

Postpartum Bipolar Disorder 315

Supporting Your Partner Postpartum 317

Takeaways. 319

16 | Romantic Relationships. 321

Why Is My Relationship Different? 322

Changing How You Communicate. 329

Rupture and Repair with Your Kids 335

Navigating Maternal Gatekeeping 336

Postpartum Intimacy 344

Attachment Styles and Your Relationship 348

How to Keep Your Connection. 353

Takeaways. 355

17 | Returning to Work 357

What Does Maternity Leave Look Like?. 358

The Mixed Emotions in Returning to Work. 362

Balancing Act 369

Return-to-Work Coping Plan 372

Takeaways. 379

18 | Baby Sleep (and Your Own Sleep Deprivation). 381

Safe Sleep Guidelines 382

Our Sleep Stories 383

What Exactly *Is* Sleep Training? 385

Deciding What's Right for You. 387

Bedtime Routine and Baby Sleep 389

Combatting Sleep Deprivation 391

Takeaways. 398

19 | **Social Support. 401**

Our Friendship Experiences Postpartum. 402

You've Got a Friend in Me. Do I Have a Friend in You? 405

The Common Friendship Concerns of Motherhood. 408

Takeaways. 421

Our Goodbye. 423

References 425

Introduction

The mom who stands over her baby's bassinet at night to make sure she is still breathing.

The mom who tells her partner, "I just don't feel like myself."

The parents who look at each other after their baby is born, thinking, *What did we do? We were not expecting this.*

The mom sitting alone in the NICU hospital room, asking herself, *What did I do wrong?*

The mom who is so terrified to experience birth trauma again that she decides not to expand the family she always wanted.

The dad looking at his new baby, feeling paralyzed with anxiety and unable to help his partner.

This book is for all of you. We see you, parents. We *were* these parents. We are here for you.

As two registered psychologist moms, we came together in 2020 to form an Instagram page related to motherhood and maternal mental health. Seven hundred posts; countless guests, podcasts, interviews; and over 278,000 followers (and growing) later, we are excited to put our hard work—and our firsthand discussion with postpartum parents—into a workbook that is relatable, practical, backed by research, and accessible to parents.

Our experience in the world of postpartum mental health began when we each decided to start a family. Given our background and training, we felt we were both fairly resourced people, but our individual experiences with pregnancy, birth, and the NICU rocked our worlds. This led us to take a deeper dive into the resources and material available for postpartum mothers, and we found that it lacked a very specific type of resource—one that encompasses maternal mental health and that does not solely focus on postpartum depression. What we have heard from postpartum mothers around the world is that there is so much more to the fourth trimester beyond postpartum depression.

Advancements have finally begun to shed light on postpartum mental health. But when Caitlin was a new mom in 2017, grappling with what likely would have been diagnosed as postpartum anxiety, she struggled to find information that felt right for *her*. The information she searched was not backed by sound research, and the material felt outdated and distant—not written by moms who are currently experiencing what motherhood is like in this generation. She desperately needed a resource that addressed the topics of motherhood that are often not talked about: the anxiety, intrusive thoughts, stress of breastfeeding, social media comparisons, and overwhelming guilt and shame that go along with the expectations of motherhood. Our hope is that this book fills that void by providing real, honest, and raw insights into motherhood in a nonjudgmental way.

Additionally, it is our hope that this book reaches the "new mom" who is wondering if these feelings are normal, the "seasoned mom" who is still traumatized from the birth experience she never expected, and the "expectant mom," who wants to prepare for the postpartum period and learn how to say no to boundary violators. There is an overload of online information available to parents, and we know firsthand that this overabundance of information can lead down a deep, dark rabbit hole, often fueling feelings of anxiety, shame, and inadequacy. We have come together to provide information that is sound, reputable, evidence based, and provided by moms who are not only mental health professionals, but who also are in the thick of it, who have lived through what we write about.

The entry into motherhood is met with fatigue as parents juggle multiple appointments, and therapy can often fall to the wayside. We hope that the practical and relatable aspect of this book can reach new moms and give them the skills and tools to thrive during this period. We also invite parents to follow us on our Instagram page (@mamapsychologists) and become part of our community. Our goal is for everyone who comes in contact with us to feel less alone on the journey of motherhood.

WHOM THIS BOOK IS FOR

This book is intended for two audiences. The first is parents (especially mothers) in the perinatal period, which is an all-encompassing term that refers to the period of time that starts at pregnancy and extends up to 12 months postpartum. However, we recognize that there are many parents who have not healed in that time frame. Therefore, this book is also for all parents who are struggling with postpartum mental health disorders, birth trauma, or the challenges of motherhood. This audience is intentionally very broad because it is our hope that this book will cover as many issues as possible that parents face. We want any parent who picks up our book to flip through it and think, This is it! This is what I need right now.

The second audience is health care professionals who support parents in the postpartum period. We have heard from many parents, mothers in particular, who have felt like their experience has not been listened to or validated by their health care providers. Our hope with this book is that every therapist or health professional who reads it will use it as a reference when looking for symptoms of postpartum mental health disorders, for examples of how to work through the many myths of motherhood, and as a starting point when seeing women with birth trauma.

For mental health professionals in particular, this book will provide several unique exercises that they can work through with their clients, including trauma-informed interventions that are both body-centered and cognition-centered, as well as psychoeducational talking points. These exercises can be done either in session or assigned as homework between sessions. When used in a group setting, our intention is that each different chapter can be a topic for discussion, with exercises serving as an important addition to therapeutic support.

WHAT IS IN THIS BOOK

In these pages, we will take a deep dive into the expectations and myths of motherhood, as well as issues surrounding mom guilt and the familiar shame of being a parent. We will explore a variety of postpartum mental health concerns, including anxiety, depression, obsessive-compulsive disorder (OCD), and birth trauma. We will further explore the stress and anxiety in areas like feeding, sleeping, and navigating relationships. We will focus a large portion on coping with birth trauma and negative thoughts, as well as how to build your support system.

To address these topics, you will find that we integrate a variety of therapeutic tools throughout these pages, including those that borrow from the fields of mindfulness, cognitive behavioral therapy (CBT), somatic psychology, relational therapy, and eye movement desensitization and reprocessing (EMDR) therapy. These methods will provide you with quick coping skills you can add into your day-to-day routine to feel more grounded and emotionally centered. You'll also find tips to help you explore how your thoughts impact your mood and behavior, as well as tools to recognize the warning signs that you are becoming triggered or overwhelmed. Finally, you'll learn strategies to manage any challenging family or interpersonal dynamics that arise on your journey through motherhood.

There is no right way to approach this book. You can start at the beginning or jump right to whatever need is the hungriest. Start wherever feels right for you or on whatever topics you feel would help you navigate motherhood the best.

Mom life feels hard because it *is* hard. You are not your symptoms or your thoughts. There is hope, and we are here to give it to you.

My birth experience wasn't as bad as _____.

I am sure this is how everyone feels after their birth experience.

It could have been so much worse than it was.

But I have my beautiful baby; I shouldn't feel the way that I do.

Shouldn't I just be over it by now?

I don't even know what to call my birthing experience, but I just knew I wasn't okay.

1   Birth Trauma

If you have ever thought some of these things to yourself, you are not alone. Some of the most frequent questions we hear relate back to the birth experience and the trauma that can surround it. You might be wondering what exactly birth trauma is, or how you even know if you've experienced it. It can feel like such a big and daunting question. Our goal for this chapter is to provide you the opportunity to explore what birth trauma is, how it can present, and the ways to support yourself if you are working to heal from it.

WHAT IS BIRTH TRAUMA?

Birth trauma refers to any experience during the labor process where the mother or the child's life is in actual danger or is perceived to be in danger. This is an experience that can be traumatic for you *and* your partner. Some factors that make birth trauma more likely include:

- Medical complications during pregnancy and birth
- Premature birth
- NICU stay
- Previous trauma
- Baby requiring treatment by professionals after birth
- Stillbirth
- Lengthy or painful labor
- Unexpected change in birth plan

- Need for medical intervention during labor
- Previous pregnancy loss or miscarriage
- Infertility

Maybe you had planned for a home birth and ended up needing an emergency C-section at the hospital. Maybe you had a preterm baby who needed to spend time in the NICU. Maybe you didn't feel respected or heard by medical professionals. Maybe you had suffered through previous miscarriages or pregnancy loss, and giving birth was terrifying. Maybe your baby stopped breathing during labor and you feared for their life. Or maybe you hemorrhaged and feared for your own life.

Whatever level of birth trauma you experienced, we believe it matters and should be honored. We can turn the common phrase a little, saying "Trauma is in the eye of the beholder," and as far as we are concerned, this sentiment could not be truer. To allow us the opportunity to conceptualize what birth trauma can look like, let us share with you Chelsea's own experiences:

I honestly have mixed feelings about my birth experience. From an outside perspective, it was truly traumatic. I went into spontaneous preterm labor in the middle of the night at 27 weeks and 5 days pregnant. There was no anticipation, no preparation, and a lot of chaos. We were two-and-a-half hours away from the nearest hospital with a Level III NICU—which is where my son needed to be— and I was no longer in a place to be transported at 5 centimeters dilated.

I remember the fear, the chaos, the tears, and the uncertainty that hung in the air. My doctor looked my husband and me in the eye and said, "We don't know what is going to happen or what the baby will look like."

It almost felt like she was telling us to hope for the best but prepare for the worst. We waited for labor to progress, trying to slow it down long enough for the neonatal trauma transport team to arrive. Time felt slow and fast all at the same time. I truly feel like there were a lot of traumas throughout the experience. However, I felt so respected and supported during my labor process that I felt some of my well-being was protected through that.

Sometimes it can take some time to know whether birth trauma was a part of your experience. So if you're unable to realize it or reflect on it right away, that is okay. There is no time frame for this understanding. However, there are a few hallmark signs and symptoms of birth trauma provided here. You'll notice that we've also included some more positive emotions that can arise as part of birth trauma, as you can have a mixture of both positive and challenging emotions. A common misconception is that the *entire* birth experience must be viewed as traumatic or else it doesn't count as "trauma." This is simply not true. There can be moments of your birth experience that you feel content with or even positive about. Other aspects you might not remember so fondly. This is natural and normal—these experiences *can* coexist together.

SIGNS AND SYMPTOMS OF BIRTH TRAUMA

Place a check mark by the following experiences that you feel apply to your situation. There is no right way to think or feel when processing your birth experience. We've provided space for any additional feelings or concerns that we may not have covered.

- ☐ Insomnia
- ☐ Flashbacks or nightmares of the birthing experience

- ☐ Feeling a sense of unreality or detachment
- ☐ Avoidance of previously enjoyed activities
- ☐ Avoidance of social interactions
- ☐ Feeling on edge
- ☐ Anxiety
- ☐ Depression
- ☐ Feelings of failure
- ☐ Difficulty with decision-making
- ☐ Feelings of grief or loss
- ☐ Gratitude or gratefulness for your baby, your health, or certain parts of birth experience
- ☐ Physical difficulties related to recovery
- ☐ A change in future family planning goals
- ☐ Relationship difficulties
- ☐ Shame or guilt
- ☐ Relief
- ☐ Exhaustion
- ☐ Difficulty connecting with the baby
- ☐ Other: _____
- ☐ Other: _____

YOUR BIRTH EXPERIENCE

If it feels safe and comfortable to do so, we invite you to take a moment to dig deeper and reflect on additional aspects of your birth experience. If this feels too uncomfortable, it is more than okay to skip this part. If you see a therapist and want to do this activity during a session, that can be helpful for some people. Proceed in whatever way feels best for you, as we know this is an extremely challenging topic.

When you think back to your birth experience, what emotions come up?

_____

_____

_____

_____

As you reflect on your birth experience, do any memories seem "stuck," feel difficult to think about, or cause an unexpected emotional reaction?

_____

_____

_____

_____

_____

When you think back to your birth experience, what sensations did you notice in your body?

_____

_____

_____

_____

_____

_____

Do you find yourself being triggered by certain situations, events, or people related to your birth experience? For example, do you have difficulties discussing your birth experience, being around someone who is pregnant or has a newborn, or going to doctor's appointments?

_____

_____

_____

_____

_____

_____

Are there aspects of the birth experience that you wish you could change? Are there any aspects that you feel grateful for?

_____

_____

_____

_____

_____

_____

_____

BUT I HAD A "TYPICAL" BIRTH—WHY DO I FEEL THIS WAY?

You can have a positive outcome—in other words, you can take home a happy and healthy baby—and still feel like your birth experience was negative. People are often told, "Well, you have a healthy baby, why do you feel that way?" or "You should be grateful that you *have* a baby." However, just because you're grateful that you have a healthy baby doesn't mean that you can't grieve or be affected by your birth experience. You can feel two seemingly conflicting emotions, and that is perfectly normal.

There are so many different scenarios that can lead to a traumatic birth experience that it will be a really individualized experience. That's where the previous reflection questions become important. It will allow you the opportunity to explore how *you* feel about the experience—because that's what matters.

CAN I PREVENT IT?

Unfortunately, there is no magic pill or method that will prevent birth trauma. Often, part of the problem is that it is a highly unexpected experience—just as you cannot prevent it, you also cannot fully predict it. All that being said, there are some things we recommend doing during pregnancy to help you prepare:

- Start working with a therapist early on if this resource is available to you. Therapists who have been trained to work with trauma (especially birth trauma) will be able to support you in exploring, processing, and gaining the tools you need to begin moving through your healing journey.

- Write down any questions or concerns that you may have about the birthing experience, and discuss these with your birth support team, including your OB-GYN, doula, or midwife. This is especially helpful if you experienced birth trauma with a previous child and are trying to conceive again. While it is often most helpful to discuss these concerns during pregnancy, you can also do so during the postpartum period. Asking a professional any questions you may have about what happened during the birthing experience, including *why* it happened, may help provide comfort or clarity.

- Create a postpartum coping plan, which can provide you with a template of resources and coping strategies that you can keep on hand (see chapter 15). This can relieve some of the pressure of trying to find ways to cope when you are in the thick of the postpartum period. It also provides you an opportunity to understand some warning signs of perinatal mood disorders that you or your partner can look out for.

- If you have your heart set on creating a birth plan, create a list of flexible birth preferences that outlines your desires for the birthing experience but also explores alternative options for what could happen. We like the term birth *preferences*, as there can be a lot of meaning behind the word *plan*. Having some flexibility in what can happen during the birthing process can be a protective factor in managing the unexpected. A template for a flexible birth plan is provided on the next page.

Exercise
Flexible Birth Preferences

Fill out this checklist to discuss your preferences and wishes for the labor and delivery process. Be sure to take this plan with you to appointments so you can discuss options, concerns, and questions you may have about the birth experience.

Birth location:

I would like to deliver:

- ☐ At home
- ☐ At the following hospital or birthing center:

_____

_____

During labor:

I would like the following members of my support team to be present during the labor and delivery process:

_____

_____

_____

_____

_____

_____

I would like:

- ☐ Dim lighting
- ☐ Music playing
- ☐ To eat and drink if my provider allows it
- ☐ As few vaginal exams as possible
- ☐ As few interruptions as possible
- ☐ To wear my own clothing
- ☐ For my partner to photograph or film the experience

Pain management:

- ☐ Epidural
- ☐ Acupuncture
- ☐ Acupressure
- ☐ Breathing exercises
- ☐ Massages
- ☐ Whatever my doctor suggests at the time
- ☐ No pain management unless I request it

During delivery:

I would prefer the delivery planned as a:

- ☐ Vaginal birth
- ☐ C-section
- ☐ Vaginal delivery after previous C-section (VBAC)
- ☐ Water birth

Delivery position and props:

- ☐ Squatting
- ☐ On hands and knees
- ☐ Lying down
- ☐ Standing
- ☐ Birth tub
- ☐ Birth ball
- ☐ Birthing stool or chair

In case of a C-section:

If circumstances do not allow for a vaginal birth, I would prefer:

- ☐ A second opinion
- ☐ A mirror to see the baby come out
- ☐ The drapes to be lowered
- ☐ To remain conscious
- ☐ At least one of my arms to remain free

After delivery:

- ☐ Delayed cord clamping
- ☐ Allow my partner to cut the umbilical cord
- ☐ Keep the placenta
- ☐ Access to a shower

Newborn care:

- ☐ Breastfeed as soon as possible
- ☐ Bottle-feed
- ☐ Formula feed
- ☐ Have immediate skin-to-skin contact
- ☐ Have the baby be wiped clean before holding it

Of the choices you didn't check, what would you be open to if circumstances do not allow for your preferences to be upheld?

_____

_____

_____

_____

_____

_____

_____

What additional questions or concerns do you have? What other information would you like to know about?

_____

_____

_____

_____

_____

_____

_____

WHAT CAN I DO?

If you have experienced birth trauma, it is important to let your medical provider or birth support team know that there are things you are struggling with. We recommend reaching out to a trained perinatal therapist or a therapist who has experience working with birth trauma.

In addition, the following pages provide a few specific tools and exercises you can use to help you process your birth experience. These strategies are not intended to replace any recommendations of a health professional, but they can help you honor your story, reconnect with your body, and become aware of your triggers.

Exercise
Affirmations

Affirmations are positive, supportive, and encouraging statements that can help you acknowledge your experience, challenge any negative and intrusive thoughts, and calm your mind. We also like to call them *mama mantras*.

Here are a few affirmations that we recommend for birth trauma. Take some time to read these over—you can even say them out loud and highlight the ones that feel right to you. Please take what works for you, leave what doesn't, and adapt any of the statements to fit your own experience better.

May I be kind to myself.

May I find the strength I need.

There is no right way to heal.

It is not my fault.

May I find the support I need.

*I am allowed to feel disappointed;
that does not make me ungrateful.*

My struggle and story are valid.

I am allowed to grieve my birth experience.

There is no right way to grieve.

There is no timeline for my grief.

I can care for myself and my body so it may heal.

I am strong.

Exercise
Find Your Calm Place

One way to find a sense of calm in the midst of a difficult time is to create a peaceful, courageous, or safe place in your mind. It is a great tool to settle your nervous system when you are having a hard time coping or when you remember a difficult experience in your life.

Think of a place that you find very calming. It can be a place you've been to before, a place you've seen only in pictures, or any place you can imagine. Some people visualize being in the mountains, by a body of water, in their backyard, or on their couch with a loved one. There are no right or wrong answers—it just needs to feel calming to you.

Describe your calm place in a sentence or drawing.

As you think about this calm place, take a few moments to notice what you see, hear, smell, and feel. Just notice this. Pay attention to your breath. Take deep breaths in and out. See how these calming moments have changed how you envision your calm place.

Describe your calm place once more in a sentence or drawing.

Continue to focus on your calm place, imagining it with your five senses in even brighter and more vivid detail. Feel it more deeply in your body. Then think of a word or phrase that will help remind you of your calm place, and say this word or phrase to yourself as you keep focusing on the sights, smells, sounds, and feelings in your body.

Write your cue word or phrase here.

_____

Now try adding some bilateral stimulation by tapping on your knees in an alternating pattern as you hold this cue word or phrase in your mind. The tapping motions help activate your parasympathetic nervous system, which is responsible for rest and relaxation.

Continue tapping on your knees—alternating right and left—for approximately six to eight taps.

Whenever you are feeing anxious, visit your calm place, bring your cue word or phrase to mind, and do some alternating taps on your knees.

Exercise
Finding Your Container

The container exercise is a helpful tool you can use whenever you need a place to temporarily "contain" or place any difficult thoughts, feelings, or memories. It can create a bit of space from whatever is bothering you until you can put in the time and energy needed to address it at a later date.

To start, bring to mind some sort of a container that can hold whatever is troubling you. Your container can be a room, a plastic storage bin, a drawer, or a treasure chest—anything big and strong enough to hold whatever you need it to in this moment.

Describe your container in a sentence or drawing.

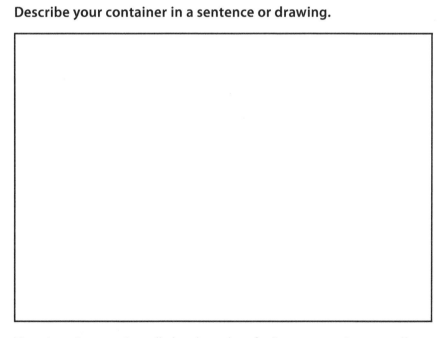

Now imagine putting all the thoughts, feelings, sensations, smells, or sounds that need to go in there. Take a couple of deep breaths.

Is there anything else that needs to be placed in the container? If so, write or draw it here.

Then imagine securely closing the container and putting it back where it belongs. Maybe you place it on a shelf, send it out to sea, or close the door to the room.

How do you feel now? Take a few moments to write or draw how you are feeling.

Take a few more deep breaths. Know that whatever is distressing you is held securely in this container until you feel ready to handle it.

Exercise
5-4-3-2-1 Grounding

Whenever you feel caught up in distressing memories or flashbacks, grounding exercises are a great way to orient yourself to the present moment and calm your nervous system.

To start, rate your level of distress on a scale of 1 to 10, with 1 being *little or no distress* and 10 being *extreme distress*.

I am at a _____.

Then go through the following five steps:

Name five things you can see:

_____

_____

_____

_____

_____

Name four things you can hear:

_____

_____

_____

_____

Name three things you can touch:

_____

_____

_____

Name two things you can smell:

_____

_____

Name one thing you can taste (or you can write down one of your favorite statements from the previous affirmations exercise):

_____

_____

_____

_____

_____

Rate yourself again now that you are more grounded.

I am at a _____.

WHAT ABOUT MY PARTNER?

If your partner feared for your life or your child's life during the birthing process, they may also experience the effects of birth trauma, even long past the birth itself. You may notice that they experience similar symptoms as you, including helplessness, detachment, and hypervigilance, many of which stemmed from the loss of control over the situation (including fears about what could have happened to you or your baby). It can be difficult for them to juggle transitioning into parenthood, continuing with their responsibilities outside the home, and also supporting you while they navigate their own birth trauma.

There is also a lack of awareness and stigma around asking for help among partners who have experienced birth trauma. Sometimes partners feel as though they can't reach out for support because they feel like their experience is less valid; they may feel undeserving of attention since they weren't the one giving birth or because they feel they are supposed to be the "strong partner" at this time. They may even feel somehow culpable because they weren't able to protect their partner from the traumatic experience. Or perhaps they simply don't know what to ask for.

Here are some ways you can encourage your partner to get support:

- Go through this chapter with them. See what their responses are.
- Do not dismiss their individual experience, feelings, or thoughts.
- Try to keep an open line of communication between the two of you in terms of how each of you are coping.
- Encourage them to engage in positive self-care activities, such as exercising, eating well, showering, and sleeping. It is important to ensure that these basic needs are being met to facilitate their well-being. In addition, encourage them to do tasks that involve

connecting and bonding with the baby, such as getting baby up after sleep, dressing baby, bathing baby, or enjoying skin-to-skin contact with baby.

• Encourage them to reach out to support groups geared toward dads or partners in your area, as it can be helpful for them to connect with another parent who has gone through the same journey as them. Should they need more intensive therapeutic support, encourage them to reach out to a trained professional.

TAKEAWAYS

We hope that this chapter provided you with some insight into birth trauma and what it might look like for you. We wanted to provide you with this information and education so you could put a name to what you have been or are currently experiencing.

Remember, you do not have to suffer alone or in silence. If you feel like any of the information in this chapter resonated with you, reach out to local supports to help you explore your birth experience. You have every right to feel heard and validated within your birth experience, so don't be afraid to speak out and share your story.

OUR FAVORITE RESOURCES

- Postpartum Support International (www.postpartum.net)

- The Good Men Project (www.goodmenproject.com)

- *The Postpartum Husband* by Karen Kleiman

- *What About Us?* by Karen Kleiman

I hate the way my body looks now as a mother.

I thought I would snap right back and the weight would just go away.

I was never really prepared for these changes!

And these societal expectations for me to look the same...or even better?!

2   Body Image

Do any of these phrases sound familiar to you? Have you ever sat on the sidelines or stayed out of the swimming pool out of fear of what your body looks like? If so, please know that there are so many mothers like you out there. Maternal and postpartum body image (and general body image overall) can take a significant toll on women's mental health. Especially after pregnancy, women are expected to "bounce back" better than before. That's because we live in a world that objectifies nearly every part of the female body. Women are expected to live up to idealistic beauty standards, and this message is plastered across social media pages, TV shows and movies, advertisements, and even magazines at the grocery store check-outs.

However, we want you to know that most of the curated images of pregnant and postpartum women do not indicate what happens for every body. In this chapter, we break down some of the stigmas related to body image, explore societal expectations for women, look at scenarios that may feel triggering for you, and more.

WHAT IS BODY IMAGE?

Body image refers to how you feel about yourself and the extent to which you feel comfortable in your own skin. It is not just about believing that your body is good—it is about *knowing* and *feeling* the goodness of your body.

When it comes to postpartum body image, there are a lot of factors at play that can make it tough to accept your body. Think about it: You just pushed a human from your body, your hormones are going wild, and you're adjusting to a new life (whether it's your first child or not). Throw in some societal expectations, personal standards, and social media comparisons, and you have a recipe for feeling all kinds of emotions about your postpartum body.

It is extremely likely to see at least some physical changes to your body after pregnancy. Some of these changes may include:

- Weight fluctuations
- Stretch marks
- Breast changes
- Nipple changes
- Vaginal changes
- Episiotomy
- C-section scar
- Loose or sagging skin
- Loss of or changes to hair
- Hormone changes

This is by no means an exhaustive list, as every body—and every birth experience—is different. After taking a look at these changes, and considering your own experience, take a moment to reflect on the roller-coaster your physical body took from pre-pregnancy to pregnancy to postpartum.

In addition to all these physical changes taking place, it can become difficult to accept your body when you receive messages from a variety of different sources that affect how attractive you feel. For example, your partner, family, or friends may make comments that make you feel pressured to lose the baby weight and "bounce back." This is often complicated by unrealistic images of the female body, specifically the postpartum body, that are portrayed in the mainstream media. Magazine covers routinely showcase celebrities' bodies after they've had a baby, publicizing all the baby weight they lost in two months. It is images like this that can lead postpartum mamas into a comparison trap.

When you consider the messaging that surrounds pregnancy, you might think of phrases like "Big bellies are beautiful" and "Eat for two." But what about the messaging that surrounds the postpartum body? Is the media telling you that your post-baby body is beautiful? Most often, it is not, and that's simply an awful feeling for any postpartum mom.

What is the messaging you have heard around pregnant bodies?

_____

_____

_____

_____

_____

_____

What is the messaging you have heard around postpartum bodies?

_____

_____

_____

_____

_____

COMMON POSTPARTUM BODY STRUGGLES

Given the objectification of the female body, there is a lot of advertising geared toward postpartum moms that promote the "need" to get their body back. Countless members of our community have shared stories of being preyed upon by companies selling weight loss products, miracle shakes, or some type of body-shrinking wrap.

When women are continually subjected to this message that they need to "bounce back," they can begin to struggle with body image. The initial reactions to these messages can eventually become more ingrained into women's thought patterns, which can lead to:

- Decreased sexual activity or intimacy with their partner
- Avoidance of activities
- Lower self-esteem
- Lower confidence
- Feelings of shame
- Inability to wear clothing they like

- Intrusive or negative thoughts
- Feelings of disconnection from their body
- Feelings of grief and loss related to what their body used to do or look like
- Restricted or unhealthy eating habits
- Buying products to "fix" themselves
- Believing that they need to hide

Let's break down a couple of the struggles that we hear quite often after women have a baby:

1. **I feel uncomfortable or unable to have sex with my partner.** Intimacy after having a baby can be a source of stress and contention between couples. There are many biological and psychosocial changes that can impact a mother's sexual functioning in the postpartum period, including lowered sex drive, exhaustion, disconnection from their body, hormonal changes, identity changes due to parenthood, lack of social support, body shame, relationship dissatisfaction, or a traumatic birth or stressful postpartum period (McBride & Kwee, 2017). It may take a bit of time to get back to what was normal before pregnancy or giving birth. It's also possible that you won't return to that old "normal"—instead you and your partner can work together on finding a new normal. Rebuilding intimacy or finding new ways to be intimate can be challenging, but here are some things that can help:

   - **Treat yourself with grace and kindness.** Remember that it may take time for your sex drive to return. Sometimes the pressure you put on yourself to have sex can make it even more challenging to have it. The six-week postpartum wait is not necessarily for everyone. Women often describe needing more recovery time, and if that is your experience, that is completely normal.

- **Reconnect as a couple.** Remember the ways that you were able to connect with your partner before having a baby and find ways to do this again. This can be as simple as making time for a five-minute conversation at the end of the day, going on a date, or even just sending check-in texts throughout the day.

- **Find new ways to be intimate.** Not all intimacy needs to necessarily involve sexual intercourse. Are you able to hug, hold hands, or even have intimate conversations? Finding different ways to be close can be helpful when sex doesn't feel comfortable or isn't an option.

- **Go to couples counseling.** If it is available to you, couples therapy is a great way to navigate these tricky issues with a neutral third party.

- **Make sure to take time for yourself.** It can be exhausting to raise a family, and when you don't have the opportunity to take care of your own basic needs, it can add a layer of difficulty to being intimate with your partner.

- **Seek support.** Do not hesitate to ask for help if physical or emotional trauma is a barrier. The body can physically hold onto the experience of trauma, making it difficult to connect with your partner. If you experienced emotional or physical trauma during your perinatal journey, therapy can help you reconnect with your body.

- **Take a social media break.** If you notice that there are certain social media accounts that add fuel to the fire for you, either mute them, take social media breaks, or delete your accounts.

Be sure to also check out chapter 16 for more information on how to navigate relationship hurdles during the postpartum period.

2. **I feel disconnected from or uncomfortable with my body.** The female body undergoes some extreme physical and emotional changes throughout the perinatal period. As a result, mothers can often feel disconnected from their body when it no longer matches what it used to look like. Throw in some unrealistic cultural standards, and what you think you should look like versus what you actually look like can feel miles apart. The following are some examples of language that might indicate you feel disconnected from your body:

- "Healing is taking longer than I anticipated."
- "I don't feel as confident as I used to."
- "I didn't want a C-section, and now I have a scar reminding me."
- "I am worried about what my vaginal area looks like after an episiotomy."
- "Why can't I lose the postpartum weight?"
- "My clothes don't fit."
- "I still don't feel like my body is my own."
- "I don't think this is how I am supposed to look."

Reconnecting with your body and reclaiming satisfaction with your body can feel difficult, but it is possible. Here are some things you can do to help:

- **See a pelvic health physiotherapist.** As we'll touch on in the next section, a pelvic floor therapist can help you heal from any lingering physical discomfort and pain. They can also help you regain trust in your body.

- **Find ways to be comfortable in your skin and increase your body confidence.** Although this may sound challenging—and it definitely can be—it is not impossible! For example, consider buying a few staple clothing pieces that fit your body now (instead of feeling frustrated with clothes that don't fit). You can also consider following "body positive" accounts online that help you feel proud of what your body has accomplished.

- **Set small, realistic goals.** Instead of trying to overhaul your body overnight, start with body movement exercises or even breathing exercises. Attempting to make a big lifestyle or diet change can feel really overwhelming, especially in the postpartum period.

- **Consider engaging in meditation or yoga practices.** These simple yet powerful approaches can help you focus on relaxing your body and getting in touch with it once again.

- **Practice body-related affirmations.** Affirmations are a great way to reconnect with your body and provide yourself with some self-compassion. We offer some simple body-related affirmations in the "How to Cope with Body Image Struggles" section of this chapter.

PELVIC FLOOR HEALTH IS IMPORTANT TOO

First and foremost, we want to preface this section by acknowledging that we are not physiotherapists, nor is this our area of expertise. However, we want to take a moment to highlight the importance of pelvic floor health as it relates to body image. Birth, at the very least, is a physically traumatic event to your body. This can have lasting effects in many areas of your life, one of which is your pelvic floor. (Hello to all the mothers who say, "Peeing when we cough is just a way of life!") However, advancements, awareness, and education in the medical field have provided an opportunity to show that women do not have to suffer in silence with pelvic floor concern.

Having a pelvic floor physiotherapist can be an important resource if you are struggling with any pelvic floor issues, including incontinence, vaginismus, sexual dysfunction, constipation, lower back pain, or pelvic organ prolapse. Unsure of what a pelvic floor physiotherapist does? Don't worry, we've got you. In general terms, a pelvic physiotherapist has specialized training regarding the pelvic floor, which is the group of muscles that comprises the bottom of your pelvis. Often, pelvic physiotherapy involves an initial internal and external exam, as well as certain exercises to help you heal from birth-related injuries and regain muscle strength in this area. We encourage you to investigate resources within your community and see if there is a pelvic floor physiotherapist who can be a part of your support team.

Pelvic floor physiotherapy can help you address any residual pain or discomfort that is interfering with your ability to connect with or regain trust in your body. After working with a trained specialist, you are likely to experience tangible shifts in your relationship with your core and pelvic floor muscles, and it can feel validating to experience these concrete improvements and feel in control of your body as you progress toward healing.

HOW TO COPE WITH BODY IMAGE STRUGGLES

If you are struggling with body image, we encourage you to work with a therapist to explore what body image means to you and how it is impacting your mental health. You might also consider working with a couples therapist to help with sex and intimacy in your relationship, or working with a pelvic floor physiotherapist to explore the physical components of your experience.

We also share some additional tools and exercises on the following pages to support you with any negative thoughts or feelings you may have toward your body. These exercises will help you respond to body image comments, challenge cognitive distortions surrounding body image, acknowledge comparisons and pressures to look a certain way, and recognize your own inner critic.

Exercise
Responding to
Body Image Comments

When you hear a triggering comment about your body, it can be challenging to know how to respond most effectively. In addition, it can trigger your own inner critic, which lowers your self-confidence and makes it difficult to get past your own shame. Even when these comments aren't made with malicious intent, navigating the conversation with the other person can feel awkward. In these cases, having some prepared statements can help you respond and feel less vulnerable in the moment.

The next time you hear a triggering comment about your body, follow these three steps to help you respond in a way that validates all your body has done for you:

1. Acknowledge the comment.
2. Redirect to a positive reframe that you feel about your body.
3. Take a deep breath, then acknowledge that your feelings around these comments are hard and may be triggering—and that's okay.

Some examples illustrating these steps are provided for you here, followed by some space for you to brainstorm your own.

Child: Mommy, do you have a baby in your belly? Why is it so big?

You: Mommy's tummy looks a little bit different than it used to. My tummy (or body) has done some amazing things—it was able to grow you!

Friend: Don't worry, you'll bounce back postpartum.

You: Thank you for trying to be supportive, but I am not focused on bouncing back right now. Motherhood has transformed me *and* my body in amazing ways, so it's not realistic for me to be the same person I was pre-baby. I am learning to honor this new version of me, and I would appreciate it if we could talk about something else.

Partner: You definitely don't look the same, but that doesn't mean it is a bad thing.

You: I understand that my body has changed since we met. That's because it actually grew a brand-new human inside of it! I am learning to celebrate what my body has accomplished, and I would appreciate it if we could focus on building intimacy back in our relationship.

Take some time to write out some prepared responses to help should you ever receive any comments about your body.

_____

_____

_____

_____

_____

_____

_____

_____

Exercise
Challenging Negative Thoughts Toward Your Body

Your inner critic is the little voice inside your head that constantly bombards you with harsh comments and feeds your negative self-dialogue. Some of these comments have even come directly from other sources, and that can make us believe they are true. When the inner critic takes over, it can lead you down a spiral of shame, grief, and disconnection. To begin the process of quieting your inner critic, you can take the following steps to challenge your negative self-talk and come up with more positive and helpful ways of viewing yourself. A hypothetical example is provided for you at each step.

Step 1: Identify the thought. Recognize a thought you have about yourself regarding body image and write it down here.

Example: *I feel disgusting in my own skin.*

_____

_____

_____

_____

_____

_____

_____

Step 2: Describe how this negative thought makes you feel. What are the different emotions you feel when you think or say this to yourself?

Example: *This thought makes me feel ashamed, sad, hurt, and unworthy.*

_____

_____

_____

_____

_____

_____

Step 3: Look at the evidence. What is the evidence to support this thought? Is anyone making you feel bad about your body? Are you creating this narrative toward yourself?

Example: *No one has told me that I'm disgusting. In fact, my partner tells me that I'm beautiful every day. It is hard to accept my new postpartum body, but no one is making me feel ashamed about it except me.*

_____

_____

_____

_____

_____

_____

Step 4: Evaluate the thought. Is this a helpful or an unhelpful thought? Will this thought help or hinder you?

Example: *This thought is unhelpful because it prevents me from spending time with my family or going to the pool with my kids.*

_____

_____

_____

_____

_____

_____

Step 5: Think of alternative perspectives. If you were talking to your best friend, what would you say if they were having this thought?

Example: *I would tell my friend that her body is amazing, not disgusting, and that the work her body did to create and sustain new life is something to celebrate.*

_____

_____

_____

_____

_____

_____

Step 6: Describe how this new perspective makes you feel. What emotions come up when you think of this new thought?

Example: *This new perspective helps me feel more grateful and accepting of my body. While I may not feel totally comfortable in my body now, I can remind myself of all that it has accomplished.*

_____

_____

_____

_____

_____

_____

Exercise
Affirmations for Body Image

Affirmations are an important way to shift your inner dialogue and create a sense of connection and kindness within yourself. Here are some more general affirmations to help you reconnect with your body, followed by some more particular affirmations that might resonate with more specific experiences. Look these over, making note of any that feel right or true for you. As always, take what works for you, leave what doesn't, and adapt any of the statements to fit your own experience better.

I am learning to connect with my body again.

It may never be the same, but I can love my body again.

My body created beautiful life, and for that I am thankful.

I can listen to my body and trust my instincts.

I am thankful for what my body can do.

I am learning to trust my body again.

I can care for myself by also caring for my body.

For an unplanned or negative C-section experience, try these out:

I am allowed to feel _____.

My body did the best it could.

I am strong.

I am allowed to grieve my birth experience.

Birth is beautiful no matter how it happened.

I am allowed to be grateful.

May my body heal.

My body did not fail me.

This is the birth my body and baby needed.

And for a planned and/or positive C-section experience, see if any of these resonate:

May my body heal.

I am grateful to have had a birth experience like this.

Birth is beautiful.

I made the right choice for me.

I am thankful for the option to choose.

I am strong.

This is the birth my body and baby needed.

TAKEAWAYS

We know that your body image can have a long-lasting effect on how you feel about yourself, what activities you participate in, how you choose to dress, and your overall mental well-being. By no means are we saying that it is easy to just change your mindset about your body, but we want you to know that it is possible. As hard as it is, there are ways to embrace the changes (including the stretch marks) and to find new ways to connect with your postpartum body.

Your body is your one and only. It was there since the day you were born. Every part of your body has a story—every scar, every stretch mark, all of it. Some of the stories may be hard, some may be funny, and some may be meaningful. But they're all stories worth listening to.

I guess we can postpone Tegan's birthday until you guys are able to come.

I have lots to do tonight, but it's okay if you come for a little bit.

Yes, I can pick that up.

We prefer to limit snacks before dinner, but one little cookie? I guess that's okay.

3   Boundaries

On the outside, you may be saying all these things with a smile, while on the inside, you're actually screaming, "No, I don't want to postpone the party! No, I don't want you to come over! No, I don't want to pick up just one more thing! No, don't give her that damn cookie! I have had it!"

How many of you resonate with this *no* screaming inside of you? This is a sign that your boundaries aren't being listened to or that you haven't let people know where your boundaries are.

We often hear our clients and the members of our social media community discuss boundary issues they struggle with. Many individuals grew up trying to please everyone, sacrificing their boundaries for the sake of others, or finding out that people are not to be trusted. Although there are entire books devoted to the topic of boundaries, this chapter will provide you the highlights: the different types of boundaries you can set, the tools you need to set them, and what to do in certain tricky situations. Let's dive in.

WHAT ARE BOUNDARIES?

A boundary is a limit that you set for yourself within your relationships or with others. It defines what you are okay and not okay with. Boundaries are important because they:

- Keep you emotionally and physically safe
- Define your role in your relationships

- Let others know what is acceptable and unacceptable
- Prevent resentment by keeping you from doing things you don't want to do

You can think of a boundary as the fence line that separates your yard from your neighbor's yard. The lawn inside your fence is yours, which you are responsible for watering and taking care of. It's not your responsibility to take care of your neighbor's lawn. Could you hop over your fence and help them out if they ask for a little assistance with pulling weeds or planting flowers? Absolutely! But at the end of the day, it is their responsibility to take care of their lawn.

One common fallacy about boundaries is that they shut people out. This is absolutely not the case. They simply let other people know where your yard ends and where their yard begins.

The concept of boundaries is difficult enough to navigate in its own right, but it gets even trickier with the fact that people keep different boundaries for different individuals. For example, the physical boundaries you have with your kids are likely much different from your physical boundaries with an acquaintance. Boundaries can become quite convoluted depending on the situation, context, and relationship with the other person.

Regardless, though, these are *your* boundaries. Different people have different tolerances for certain actions or non-actions. That is why setting boundaries is so important—not everyone knows what you find acceptable and what you do not. Take some time to reflect on the boundaries in your life.

What sort of boundaries do you have (with family, friends, work, school, etc.)?

_____

_____

_____

_____

What boundaries do you need to set but are hesitant or anxious to?

_____

_____

_____

_____

What is your inner voice telling you about setting boundaries? For example, is it saying that you are going to make the other person upset? That you are going to seem rude or ungrateful? That it's just easier to do whatever they want you to do?

_____

_____

_____

_____

TYPES OF BOUNDARIES

There are several types of boundaries that you can have, which can all vary depending on the context, situation, and person. Here are six boundaries that you deserve in your life:

1. **Physical boundaries.** Physical boundaries refer to your body and your personal bubble. Are you the type of person who likes to hug everyone? Or do you reserve physical touch for certain people? Does the thought of hugging others create feel-good emotions or make you want to back away? Especially during pregnancy, your physical boundaries can be violated by the most unexpected offenders. Have you ever had a stranger come up in your space and touch or rub your pregnant belly? In these moments, chances are you're thinking, *Get your hand off my belly, lady!*

   When was a time when your physical boundaries were violated?

   _____

   _____

   _____

   _____

   _____

2. **Emotional boundaries.** Emotional boundaries refer to the type of limits you set when it comes to sharing your feelings with others, including what you're comfortable sharing, when you choose to share it, and with whom you choose to share it. Emotional boundary

violations occur when someone tells you that your feelings are wrong, criticizes you, or puts you down.

When was a time when your emotional boundaries were violated?

_____

_____

_____

_____

_____

3. **Time boundaries:** Time boundaries refer to how you use, protect, and prioritize your time. Boundary violations occur when you overcommit yourself or when people misuse how you spend your time. Have you ever had someone say, "It will just take a minute" or "I will be there in five minutes," only for them to show up an hour later? This is a violation of time boundaries.

When was a time when your time boundaries were violated?

_____

_____

_____

_____

_____

4. **Material boundaries:** Material boundaries refer to the limits you put on your personal possessions and what you are (and are not) willing to share with others. This can include your finances, clothing, jewelry, car, and so on. For example, you might get questions like "Can I borrow that? I just need it for a couple of days and then I'll bring it back" or "Can you spot me a loan until I am paid?" Material boundaries can be violated when the other person doesn't return your money or possessions in the agreed upon time frame or in the same condition in which they were borrowed.

   When was a time when your material boundaries were violated?

   _____

   _____

   _____

   _____

   _____

5. **Mental boundaries:** Mental boundaries (often called *intellectual boundaries*) refer to the respect toward your thoughts, beliefs, and opinions. Healthy mental boundaries involve considering or at least allowing differing points of view, whereas boundary violations occur when someone dismisses or belittles what other people have to say. This boundary is violated the most often when it comes to parenting. There will always be countless opinions when it comes to breastfeeding versus formula feeding, crying-it-out versus not crying-

it-out, or bed-sharing versus sleeping alone—it seems to never end. We could devote an entire page to this!

When was a time when your mental boundaries were violated?

_____

_____

_____

_____

_____

6. **Sexual boundaries:** Sexual boundaries refer to your limitations around what you are willing to do when it comes to sex. When you set sexual boundaries, you let your partner know what you are okay with sexually and what is off limits. These boundaries may change postpartum—what felt safe, comfortable, or pleasurable pre-baby may no longer feel okay post-baby. You just birthed a baby and are healing in more ways than one, so you may feel different in your body.

When was a time when your sexual boundaries were violated?

_____

_____

_____

_____

WHY IS SETTING BOUNDARIES SO TOUGH?

Do you remember the old saying "Children are to be seen and not heard"? Historically, this has been the perspective of *many* people. They taught their children to be quiet, sit down, and be respectful. As a result, the children of these parents learned to sacrifice their needs in order to make other people happy. By forfeiting their own desires, they could ensure others would enjoy being around them and make them feel proud. However, people-pleasing children tend to grow up into people-pleasing adults, so it's no wonder that we have no idea how to set healthy boundaries!

As with so many other problematic behaviors that occur in adult life, this one typically goes back to what was modeled for you as a child. For example, people who grew up in environments where boundaries were nonexistent (or where boundaries may have even angered the family) may find it extremely difficult to set any boundaries with the people around them. However, another individual who grew up in an identical environment may develop very rigid boundaries and be closed off to others to avoid the types of violations that occurred when they were young. Alternatively, if someone grew up in a house where family members were enmeshed with one another—constantly jumping fences to tend to one another's lawns or pushing others out of the way to do things their way—it will be trickier to figure out where to set boundaries because they were always intervening to do what *they* thought should be done.

WHAT DO BOUNDARY VIOLATIONS LOOK LIKE?

Some boundary violations may be obvious, such as when someone makes rude comments or intrudes on you with their constant pushiness, but other violations can be quite a bit sneakier. A good rule of thumb to determine whether your boundaries are being violated is to explore how you feel around a certain person or situation. Are you feeling exhausted with your kids because of the expectation to play all the time? Are you dreading spending time with a certain friend because she shares everything that is going on with her but never has time to listen to you? Are you annoyed with your in-laws because they keep expecting you to bring the baby over instead of them visiting you? The annoyance, the resentment, and the anger—these are all signals telling you that you may need to set a boundary.

When it comes to boundary violations, your body tends to recognize what is going on before your thinking brain even has a chance to process it. Here are some common signs that you may need to set a boundary in a particular situation or with a certain person:

- Feeling anger in your body
- Feeling resentment building up
- Experiencing negative thoughts about yourself or others
- Feeling misunderstood
- Replaying the same angry conversation in your head
- Feeling angry around a certain person or commitment

When we asked our social media community about what they believe constitutes a boundary violation, we received a large number of submissions. And while this is completely subjective—what feels okay with one person may be not okay with another—there were some across-the-board responses about what clearly defines a boundary violation:

- When someone shares your confidential information with others
- When someone makes you feel guilty about your decisions

- When someone gaslights you (which means manipulating you by questioning your ability to perceive accurately or think rationally)
- When someone blames you for things that are clearly outside your control
- When someone brings up topics that you have told them are off limits
- When someone attempts to force you to conform to their way of thinking

When have your boundaries been violated?

_____

_____

_____

_____

_____

What was your initial feeling and reaction when this occurred?

_____

_____

_____

_____

_____

BOUNDARY VIOLATIONS AND THE NEW MOM

No one has their boundaries violated more than the new or pregnant mom—we can feel all the readers nodding along with us. That's because when you're a new mom, information is shooting at you from multiple directions, from the annoying advice you get about sleep during pregnancy ("Sleep now, because you will never sleep again!") to opinions about the brands of strollers, car seats, pacifiers, and diaper bag you should have. You are going to get bombarded with advice from your sister, your neighbor, Aunt Susie, and your best friend who has three kids under age 3. It can become overwhelming very quickly.

For example, when Caitlin was pregnant with her second child, she attended a Mommy and Me group where there was a presentation about cloth diapers, and she felt incredibly overwhelmed by the mountain of information coming at her. Cloth diaper samples were passed around, and there was a discussion about how much money these would save moms and how much better they were for the environment. But as a pregnant mom, Caitlin didn't want a presentation on cloth diapers— she need connection with other moms who were going through the same thing! The new information made her head spin, and all she could think was *Shit, another thing I did wrong. Why did I not do this with my first child? I could have saved all this money (plus the environment) on all these diapers that went into the garbage!* These thoughts swirled around for a while before she did some reframing about this. The reality is that some people want to use cloth diapers, and that is fine. But it didn't have to be right for Caitlin. It wasn't a value or priority for when she had her first kid. Plus, she didn't enjoy doing laundry, and cloth diapers will only add more loads. We share this example to illustrate that even a registered psychologist, who actually teaches other people how to recognize and reframe negative thoughts, fell victim to the mommy shame train.

So how do we get out of this shame spiral? How do we set boundaries against unwanted advice without being rude or seeming ungrateful? So many of us want to practice the ability to say no—to scream no from the top of our lungs!—but end up saying yes anyway. We want to acknowledge that setting boundaries is freaking hard! It is okay to feel anxious and unsure about it, especially if you grew up in an environment where boundaries were either very rigid or very enmeshed. It takes time and practice to feel comfortable with setting and holding your boundaries. So how do you get there? Let's take a look.

HOW TO SET A BOUNDARY

Step 1: The first step to setting boundaries is to figure out your values—to determine what you want to spend your energy, time, and money on. When you set boundaries that are truly aligned with your values, it reduces perfectionism, anxiety, and burnout.

For example, we both value playing with our kids, and as psychologists, we know and understand the power of play. Therefore, a boundary that we share is to always make time to play with our kids every day. We also value being clinically informed in our practice, so we set aside time each month that we can dedicate to professional development.

To help you get connected to your values, begin by asking yourself what it is that you want to spend your time on. What is important to you?

_____

_____

_____

_____

You can also explore your values by looking through the following values list, circling those that stand out to you:

- Adventure
- Affection
- Balance
- Career
- Community
- Creativity
- Family
- Fitness
- Friendship
- Fun
- Generosity
- Growth
- Health

- Kindness
- Leadership
- Learning
- Professional development
- Religion
- Recreation/leisure
- Service
- Sharing
- Spirituality
- Timeliness
- Travel
- Wealth
- Wisdom

Step 2: After you have identified your values, the next step is to communicate to other people what you want or need. This may come as a shock, but other people can't read your mind, so you need to speak up when your needs aren't being met—and it's best to do it before things get too overwhelming. Not too long ago, Caitlin fell into the habit of feeling like her head was going to explode, and she began yelling at her husband that she never got a break. He said, "Why didn't you just tell me that you needed a break instead of fuming inside and then exploding?" She replied, "Can't you tell?!" He then replied, "Well, I could tell you were mad about something, but I had no idea what it was." This is not a groundbreaking strategy, but it's important to actually speak up if you want other people to know what you're thinking. One way to clearly state your limits is to use the following sentence stems:

I need you to _____.

I feel _____ when _____.

I need you to _____.

When speaking up and asserting your needs, it's also important to do so without becoming defensive, blaming, or criticizing the other person. However, you should still be direct and specific in what you need. For example:

- "I feel stressed when you pop over at random times. I need you to stop coming over unannounced."
- "I feel overwhelmed when I'm always in charge of night feeds. I need you to help me out three nights per week."
- "I feel frustrated when I clean up after every meal. I need you to help me clean up the lunch dishes."
- "I need you to stop criticizing my parenting."
- "I feel upset when you talk about all the things you did differently when you raised me. I need you to point out the positive things I am doing."

Another area that we want to emphasize is the issue of unsolicited advice. As parents, you may sometimes feel uncertain about your role and what it looks like, so you may ask for advice from other more "seasoned" parents (which is perfectly fine!). If you asked for the advice, then you can either take it or leave it—the choice is yours. But if you didn't ask for it in the first place, then you want to develop an assertive statement to ward off that unsolicited advice. This statement may sound like:

- "Thank you for your opinion. We've thought a lot about what will work for us and have decided that we are going to bottle-feed."
- "Thanks for sharing—we have decided not to use cloth diapers."
- "It's okay that we don't agree. This is the choice I have made. I'm glad your choice worked for you."

When you are confident in your decision as a parent, you will avoid the comparison trap and be less impressionable to the advice and opinions of others. Use this space to develop your own statements to ward off unwanted advice:

_____

_____

_____

_____

_____

_____

_____

SETTING BOUNDARIES IN DIFFERENT AREAS OF YOUR LIFE

Just as many other areas of your life change after becoming a mom, you should be prepared for possible changes in the relationships you have with those around you. For instance, you may not get to spend as much one-on-one time with your partner anymore. Perhaps your mother-in-law suddenly wants to see a lot more of you for some reason. As you begin to play a new role in your own life—as a parent—you will also play a different role in their lives as well. This does not mean that everything needs to change between you and the people you interact with. However, you may need to adjust some of the boundaries you have, being sure to communicate these changes with the people who will be affected.

Setting Boundaries with Your Partner

We have heard from countless parents who hadn't experienced boundary issues with their partner until children came along. Oftentimes, these couples didn't realize how different their parenting styles would be. Here are a few of the many messages we have received from our social media community regarding boundaries in their romantic relationships. These are parents who feel that their partners are not hearing them, seeing them, or acknowledging the work they do day in and day out. Some are criticizing, while others are just plain not recognizing the impact of their words or actions:

- "Things have changed between my partner and me since baby came. I feel so resentful. She doesn't appreciate the things I do."
- "He invited six of his friends over for dinner! Four weeks after I had the baby!"

- "My partner wants to have sex right at the six-week check-up. He has joked about it a few times. I am so uncomfortable!"
- "He criticizes my parenting. Apparently, the kids only cry when I am around!"

The reality is, many issues pop up after having children that weren't there before, or that were easier to navigate before children, and this can cause your relationship dynamics to shift. If this sounds like your situation, it can be helpful to come up with sample scripts for hot-button issues that often arise. One way to clearly state your limits in these situations is to use the same sentence stem we discussed earlier:

I need you to _____.

I feel _____ when _____.

I need you to _____.

For example:

- "I feel overwhelmed when you talk about having sex right after my check-up. I need you to stop bringing it up."
- "I feel like I am giving so much of my energy during this transition. It's been hard for both of us; no one expected it would be this hard. I need to take some time for myself every day to do _____ so I can recharge."
- "I feel frustrated when your parents constantly bring up our parenting skills. It's important to me that we come at it as a team. I need us to figure out a phrase we both can use with them that is assertive."

Setting Boundaries with Your Children

So many moms have told us, "I always feel like a bad mom when my toddler reacts negatively to a boundary I set" or "I can't handle it when they push back, I always give in." However, the reality is that the most loving thing you can do for your children is to set firm, consistent, and loving boundaries. Boundaries are not meant to punish anyone. They are there to keep children safe and secure.

Plus, it is okay for your kids to be mad about boundaries! This was a huge *aha* moment in Caitlin's own life that really changed her parenting. When her toddler was younger, he would protest after supper every night and demand Cheerios, even after he'd been told that he could only have a banana for a nighttime snack. Every night when 7:00 p.m. would hit, he'd proclaim, "I want Cheerios," and when he was told no, the meltdown would begin. He would throw himself on the ground, scream, and cry—the whole shebang. Sound familiar?

In these moments, it is tempting to give in. As parents, we often feel like we can't handle another screaming fit, and we want to do just about anything to stop the tantrum. In these moments, take a deep breath and repeat the following mama mantra to yourself: "I set the boundary, and he is allowed to be upset about it." It is okay that your child is upset. Your child is allowed to have big feelings. Big feelings are okay! But when you are scared of your children's tantrums and avoid setting healthy boundaries because you can't handle the big feelings, you are teaching your kids that expressing their emotions makes them difficult to manage. and for your child, it is so scary to think, *My big feelings are too much for even my parents to handle.*

That's why it is important to set healthy boundaries and to hold the boundary firmly in place, even when your child pushes back. Holding a boundary with your kid might look like this:

"You are angry. You are allowed to be angry, but you are not allowed to hit."

The pushback: "No! Get away!"

"It's okay to feel angry. I am going to move your body to keep you safe."

The pushback: "No! NO!"

"I hear you want to play so, so much. Mom is taking a mommy break. I will be back in 30 minutes. Dad is here for you now."

The pushback: "No! NO! I want Mommy, not Daddy, Mommy!"

"I hear you want Mommy. I am taking a break. See you in 30 minutes."

Setting Boundaries with Your Friends

Does it make you feel uncomfortable to say no to your friends? Do you find that you are often agreeing to things (plans, activities, opinions) you don't want? It can sometimes be hard to set boundaries with your friends, especially if you identify as a people-pleaser. (And so many parents we've talked to have identified as such!) When you fall into the trap of people pleasing, you allow people to take advantage of your kindness and your ability to help out. As a result, you may wind up doing things for others that they could do themselves. You may also agree with others even when you disagree with them, stay quiet when people are rude and disrespectful, and not voice your concerns. You may even end up hiding parts of yourself that you feel others may not agree with.

Oftentimes, people pleasers feel obligated to support their friends no matter the situation, whether it's promoting their Tupperware business or buying five boxes of their kid's Girl Scout cookies. If you want to do any of these things, and doing so is aligned with your values, then great! But if you are feeling a sense of "I should do this," "I can't say no," or "They did _____ for me, so I have to return the favor," remind yourself that it is okay to say no. Here are some ways to assert yourself:

- "Actually, I can't talk right now. I will let you know when I am available."

- "It is important that you don't share this with anyone else."

- "I cannot always respond right away."

- "I've decided not to purchase any _____ this year."

- "If you are frustrated, please let me know instead of keeping it inside."

- "Sorry, I've decided not to go to _____."

As you start setting boundaries, you may find that some relationships shift—some may become better, as you both begin to communicate more effectively, but some changes can cause relationships to end. Being aware of your own boundaries may also let you discover the ways that you have violated others' boundaries and become better at respecting them in return.

Setting Boundaries with Your Family

Setting boundaries with your family is a *loaded* topic. The people who fed and clothed you for years are the trickiest to set limits with. The very thought of setting boundaries may feel very incongruent within your role in your family. As a child, you may have learned to play the specific role of the "good kid" and were taught to go along with what your parents did and said. However, just because your parents raised you does not give them a free pass to override the boundaries you set.

When it comes to setting boundaries with family members, the mother-in-law issue can be especially tricky. In our online community, we constantly hear from members whose mothers-in-law compare their kids or grandkids, question their parenting decisions, or act condescending toward them or other family members.

If any of these issues resonate with you, we want to remind you that you are not being mean or causing drama by setting boundaries with your family. You are allowed to have different boundaries and beliefs than your family and still love them. Sometimes, setting boundaries can mean putting distance between you and another family member. You do not need to have relationships with toxic family members just because of the fact that they are related to you.

Setting boundaries with your parents, your extended family, or your in-laws may feel uncomfortable at first, but the more you do it, the more comfortable you will become, and the more your family will come to accept and respect your limits. To prep yourself, first reinforce your confidence as a parent: "I know my values. I am parenting with my values in mind, and that's all that matters. I deserve to be treated with respect." Then start with some smaller boundaries and gradually move onto bigger ones. Boundary-setting statements might sound like:

- "Thank you for your feedback. I know you want Stella and Marta to do well in school, but we don't compare the girls' school grades."

- "Mom, are you able to stop by a couple times a week to help out with the kids? I am feeling really overwhelmed."

- "I won't allow you to undermine my parenting. If you genuinely have a question about my parenting approach, we can talk about it. Otherwise, I need you to respect my decisions."

- "I know you want to do well by the kids, but we have decided on not spanking (or not using time-outs, etc.). This is aligned with our values as parents."

- "Thank you, I know you want to help out. I know how to _____. I need you to trust that I can figure it out."

- "Please stop coming into my relationship with my sister."

- "I need you to stop bringing up my divorce in front of the kids."

- "I know you need support, and I want you to get support, but I cannot be the one to talk about your relationship issues."

- "I know you love the kids so much and want the best for them. I just need someone to listen right now, rather than to give me advice."

Setting Boundaries with Yourself

We would be remiss if we didn't think this needed its own category. How often have you pushed yourself to your breaking point? Perhaps you've found yourself rage cleaning, throwing clothes all over the place because you can't find the exact thing you wanted, or snapping at your partner and your kids. It's safe to say that this happens to 95 percent of us!

When you're pushed past your limit, you need to set boundaries with yourself by re-examining your own expectations and asking yourself if these expectations are realistic. Would you expect a good friend to hold themselves to these same expectations? Chances are, you wouldn't. Oftentimes, you are much more compassionate with others than you are to yourself, so it's helpful to look at the situation from other angles. Here are some mantras to help yourself set boundaries with the most important person in your life—you:

- "I will remind myself that resting is productive."
- "I will ask my partner for help before I become overloaded."
- "I will take a breath before responding to a frustrating situation."
- "I will put my phone away when I am with my kids."
- "I will remind myself that it's okay to feel anxious when setting new boundaries. I can do hard things."
- "I will only seek advice from reputable sources. I will not Google things when I'm feeling anxious."

WHAT IF OTHERS DON'T RESPECT MY BOUNDARY?

Sometimes when you begin to assert your values, people may react with surprise. That's because you just blew their mind! For example, if you've always hosted Thanksgiving dinner at your house but now you're telling the family that you won't be doing it this year, be prepared for some pushback. There are always going to be people who will give you a guilt trip, make veiled criticisms, or respond with rude remarks. In fact, if you find that your boundaries are being met with lots of resistance or even plain rudeness, it can be a validating sign that those boundaries were really needed.

Your boundaries are there to protect *you*—not your sister, your boss, or your friend. You don't need to convince other people that your boundary is good for your own well-being. They don't need a TED Talk on how or why you're setting boundaries. All you need to do is set the boundary. It is their job to respect it.

But what happens when you do all the necessary steps to build yourself up and say the things you need to say, and other people *still* don't hear or respect you? When this happens, you need to make sure to put a consequence in place. The word *consequence* may sound heavy and uncomfortable, but if you continue to state the boundary and nothing changes, then you might as well be talking to a brick wall. A boundary is only as effective as your follow-through on the consequence.

As always, be sure to be firm with your statement without blaming or being overly critical (even if you feel like they might deserve it!). Here is a script of how to implement the boundary and note the consequences of continuing to violate the boundary:

I need you to _____. If you continue to _____, I will _____.

I feel _____ when you _____. I need you to _____. If you continue to _____, I will _____.

For example:

- "I need you to stop coming over unannounced. If you continue to keep coming over without calling first, I am going to have to stop answering the door."

- "I need you to respect our parenting decisions. If you continue to keep undermining our parenting, I will not bring the kids around."
- "I feel frustrated when you tell me and the kids that you are going to come for a visit but don't show up. If you continue to do this, we will have to stop planning any visits."
- "I feel upset when you comment on my child's weight. I need you to keep those thoughts to yourself. If you continue to do it, we will need to come around less often."

It is okay for other people to have feelings when you set boundaries. But those are *their* feelings that *they* need to take ownership of—not you. All you can control is how you set the boundary. You have absolutely no control over how the other person is going to react to the boundary.

TAKEAWAYS

Although there is the common misconception that boundaries are meant to punish other people, they are actually just a way of freeing ourselves. By setting boundaries, we are letting other people know exactly what we need and expect from them. We can't simply expect other people to know what we're thinking—that can set us up for disappointment. Communication is key to taking the guesswork out of the equation. As we start to set limits with others, we'll find that it is easier to respect their boundaries too.

We hope that with this chapter, you feel more comfortable setting boundaries in tricky situations. We also encourage you to check out one of our favorite boundary setters: Nedra Glover Tawwab. Her Instagram page (@nedratawwab) is filled with gold nuggets of wonderful information, and her book, *Set Boundaries, Find Peace: A Guide to Reclaiming Yourself* (2021), helps you speak up, cope with toxic relationships, and let you truly be who you want to be.

It is okay to breastfeed.

It is okay to formula feed.

It is okay to combination feed.

It is okay if you exclusively pump.

It is okay if your child needs a feeding tube.

4   Breastfeeding, Formula Feeding & More

Feeding is often a serious trigger topic in the parenting world. Everyone has their own perspective on the issue, which is informed by their own preferences, what their body allows them to do, what their child can do, and what society tells them to do. When it comes to societal expectations in particular, women are often subjected to the unhealthy narrative that "breast is best." Women will literally push their bodies and mental health to the brink because they are told that exclusive breastfeeding is the only way to go. But spoiler alert: This is far from true. All feeding methods come with their own unique set of challenges, and all have positives and negatives to them.

Whichever feeding method you use throughout your child's journey, we are here for you in this chapter. We want to explore the unique relationship that develops between the feeding method you use and your own well-being and mental health. Disclaimer: We won't be jumping into lactation type support, as that would be out of our scope of practice—this includes suggestions on latching, positioning, or the best formula to buy. Instead, this is all about mental health and feeding!

FORMS OF FEEDING

Before we dive into the impact that your feeding journey can have on your mental health, let's define different types of feeding methods:

1. **Breastfeeding.** This is often considered the gold standard of feeding methods and is typically the most desired by women. It is what you hear about the most, with the majority of women describing the pressure they feel to breastfeed. Here are some reasons for breastfeeding:

   - It's low- to no-cost
   - It transfers the mother's antibodies to the baby
   - It facilitates bonding
   - It's easily portable

2. **Formula feeding.** After breastfeeding, formula feeding is arguably the second-most popular approach to feeding. Formula feeding involves using a premade powder or liquid for your child and not feeding from the breast. Parents may choose formula feeding for a variety of reasons:

   - It supports maternal mental health
   - The mother's milk did not come in
   - The baby has difficulties with latching
   - The mother or child has medical reasons for doing so
   - It supports the partner in bonding with the baby through feeding
   - The baby has adoptive or same-sex parents

- The mother works outside the home
- There is the desire to do so

3. **Combination (combo) feeding.** Combination feeding involves the use of both breastmilk and formula to provide nutrients to the baby. Here are some reasons for combo feeding:

   - The mother or child has medical reasons for doing so
   - The mother works outside of the home
   - There is the desire for the partner to provide support with some feedings
   - The mother does not have a sufficient milk supply

4. **Exclusive pumping.** Exclusive pumping is when a mother solely pumps milk from her breast and bottle feeds it to her child, often storing it after pumping for later use. Often, there is a barrier that prevents the mother from being able to breastfeed, so she chooses to exclusively pump. Here are some questions to consider when pumping:

   - How do you feel about pumping?
   - What type of pump would work for you that is affordable?
   - How often and when do you need to pump?
   - Can you get access to a lactation consultant to support your pumping journey?
   - Who else can support you?
   - How will you store milk?

5. **Tube feeding.** A nasogastric tube is a thin tube that is placed down an infant's nose to their stomach, and milk is provided through the tube as an exclusive method or to supplement another style of feeding. Gastrostomy tubes are surgically placed through the stomach wall, whereas orogastric tubes are fed through the mouth to the stomach. An infant might require tube feeding if they:

- Exhibit challenges related to feeding
- Spend time in the NICU
- Are born prematurely
- Have an oral aversion
- Demonstrate failure to thrive
- Have neurological problems

Please note that tube feeding is a medical procedure that is determined by a physician. Here we are simply providing general information for what a family may experience. If you have any concerns about any feeding method, it is important to speak directly to your health care provider.

OUR FEEDING EXPERIENCES

Caitlin

When I had my son, I didn't really have a strong picture of what I wanted my feeding journey to look like. I thought that if I could breastfeed, great! And if I couldn't, there was always formula. Looking back, I really just didn't know. I was never around a lot of babies, I didn't have any siblings with kids, and I was the first one in my close friend group to have a baby. Basically, my experience with babies was super minimal.

My son came into the world in a fury—his birth involved a failed forceps attempt and two different vacuums to pull him to safety. The jury is still out as to exactly what happened after he was born. My husband is adamant that they wheeled me to another room to stitch me up, while I remember being stitched up in the delivery room and watching my husband try to feed our son with a premixed bottle of formula. It really is one big blur, with certain pieces being clear and the rest being fuzzy.

When we were moved to the maternity floor, I tried to get my son to breastfeed with the assistance of a nurse. I was a new mom with zero experience, and it was hard. I just couldn't get him to latch. I tried the cradle hold, the football hold, all of it, but everything was just so tricky. I stayed in the hospital three days to get some extra feeding help. I remember thinking, Why is this so flippin' hard? A boob and a hungry mouth—they go together—this really should be easier!

After we were discharged, I resigned myself to the fact that our son was probably going to be formula fed, so we ended up making a mad dash to the grocery store and threw multiple cartons of formula in the cart. However, there was a part of me that was frustrated with myself, and I continued to try to breastfeed. I did a combination of formula and breastfeeding for about three weeks, then bought a pump. After that, it was a combination of breastfeeding, pumping and bottle-feeding, and formula feeding. It was exhausting. Breastfeeding never really got easier, but we continued until he was about 10 months old. Looking back, I definitely would have asked for more support earlier on, seen a lactation consultant, and sought out support at the breastfeeding clinic.

When I had my daughter a few years later, things were vastly different. Breastfeeding came easily, and in between breastfeeding and pumping, I ended up with an overproduction, the complete opposite problem I had with my first! We breastfed until she self-weaned at about 20 months. Just because you had a tough experience with one child does not guarantee it will be tough with the next child, and vice versa.

Chelsea

I will be straightforward right out of the gates: Breastfeeding was not something my son and I ended up being successful at. I was an exclusive pumper—yes, I know this can still be considered breastfeeding, but for me it felt different—and since my son was in the NICU, he took a long time to learn how to feed. With his need for oxygen and a feeding tube coupled with his growth needs (ensuring he gained an appropriate amount of weight over time), bottle-feeding didn't come naturally.

My son spent three and a half months in the NICU, and by the time we were discharged home, he was still on a feeding tube learning how to bottle-feed. Because we were trying to ensure he got enough calories, I continued to feed him a combination of formula and breastmilk. I tried to see a lactation consultant a few times, but I honestly didn't have the mental space to learn how to breastfeed while my son was on oxygen and a feeding tube. Eventually, he figured out bottle-feeding, and the feeding tube and oxygen were gone.

I continued to pump exclusively for about eight months, and had almost enough frozen milk to last him for a year, before I made the choice to stop pumping. My supply was dropping and mentally, pumping was a significant trigger for me. I was angry every time I had to pump. Ultimately, it became a better choice to continue combination feeding with my frozen milk. There was a lot of shame and guilt that came with all these decisions—shame and guilt that my son needed a feeding tube, that he needed to be combo fed, that I couldn't figure out how (or didn't have it in me) to breastfeed. It was a tough journey, but looking back, I am proud that he has grown into a strong toddler anyway.

YOUR FEEDING JOURNEY

Now that we've shared a little bit about our journeys, let's take some time to reflect on how you'd like your feeding journey to go (if you are expecting) or to reflect on how you wanted it to go. As with all our reflections throughout this book, answer what you can and want to. Leave the questions that you don't feel comfortable answering.

What were your expectations related to feeding when you were pregnant?

_____

_____

_____

_____

_____

Did your feeding journey go as planned? Why or why not?

_____

_____

_____

_____

_____

Which method(s) of feeding did you end up utilizing?

_____

_____

_____

_____

Do you feel like your mental health was impacted by the feeding method you used? In what ways?

_____

_____

_____

_____

_____

What feelings or emotions arise when you think about feeding?

_____

_____

_____

_____

_____

Did anyone pressure you into feeling as though one feeding method was better than others? If so, who?

_____

_____

_____

_____

_____

Are you experiencing any feelings of grief or loss related to any unexpected challenges in your feeding journey?

_____

_____

_____

_____

_____

In order to help you on your feeding journey (or to help you prepare for any future feeding journeys), we encourage you to do a quick online search for feeding resources in your community. Write down any services you may want to remember. For example, we would recommend looking into La Leche League or KellyMom, and you can always request more information and resources from your local health professionals.

DYSPHORIC MILK EJECTION REFLEX VS. BREASTFEEDING AVERSION

Have you heard of dysphoric milk ejection reflex (D-MER) before? Most people haven't, so if you are in that category, you are not alone. D-MER is a sudden drop of emotions that occurs when milk is released in the ducts. This often lasts for no more than a few minutes during the initial let-down reflex, but it can feel extremely triggering. Women experience a wide range of negative emotions such as anger, hopelessness, or self-loathing. These uncomfortable or unpleasant feelings are likely linked to reductions in dopamine that occur during let-down (Heise & Wiessinger, 2011), but since D-MER is a more recently described phenomenon, research is a bit limited.

Most lactating women describe being able to manage this condition more easily once they can name it and are aware that it is not their fault. If you are experiencing D-MER, we encourage you to discuss this with your health care provider for additional support, especially if your symptoms are severe.

It is important to note that D-MER is different from breastfeeding aversion, which has been described as negative feelings and intrusive thoughts that are triggered when breastfeeding (Yate, 2017). Unlike D-MER, which occurs during the let-down period and then dissipates, breastfeeding aversion persists until the baby unlatches from the breast.

Some symptoms of this phenomenon can include:

- Anger
- Disgust
- Agitation
- Guilt

- Shame
- Itching or crawling sensations on the skin
- The desire to throw or de-latch the child from skin
- The desire to run away
- Confusion

There is currently no known cause of breastfeeding aversion. As with D-MER, this is a more recently described experience, so more information and research is needed. There is often a lot of anxiety and shame associated with breastfeeding aversion, so it is important to talk to your doctor or lactation consultant if these feelings are coming up for you.

FEEDING AND MENTAL HEALTH

Breastfeeding—and we would argue all types of feeding methods—have a bidirectional relationship with mental health. What does that mean? That means that feeding can impact mental health, and mental health can also impact feeding. For example, if the feeding method you ended up using wasn't the one you had hoped for, this can increase your risk for developing postpartum depression or anxiety. At the same time, if you are struggling with a perinatal mood disorder during the postpartum period, this may interfere with your ability to breastfeed your baby.

Because there is a lot of stigma and pressure surrounding feeding and how people want and think it should go, it is common for women to experience shame and guilt, especially when it comes to breastfeeding. Women often describe feeling shamed by others for choosing a different feeding method, for how long they choose to use it, and for "not trying hard enough" to breastfeed. They are also often plagued by an inner voice telling them that the method they chose was wrong or that they are not doing what's best for their child.

Feeding may be triggering, but that doesn't mean you have to suffer in silence. Here are some of the top things we suggest doing when your emotions get big in relation to feeding:

- Gently remind yourself that it is okay not to do what others around you have done.
- Provide yourself with some self-compassion by speaking to yourself as you would to a good friend.
- Recognize that feeding is a skill and that there may be some ups and downs related to the process.
- Explore your options: Is combo feeding or formula feeding an option for you?
- Look into resources in your community, such as dietitians, lactation consultants, your child's pediatrician, or trained psychologists or social workers. You can also find resources online or in books.

In addition, we've provided some tools and exercises on the following pages to help you manage your thoughts and emotions related to feeding, including some feeding-specific affirmations, a thought-reframing exercise, and a flexible feeding plan.

Exercise
Affirmations for Feeding

Affirmations will likely pop up a lot throughout this book, as we are big believers in using them. Here are a few we recommend related to feeding. As always, take what works for you, leave what doesn't, and adapt any of the statements to fit your own experience better.

Other people's feeding methods do not need to dictate mine.

I can explore what options work for me and my child.

This is the right feeding method for me and my child.

My body did not fail me.

I have the right to choose which method works for me.

I am allowed to feel disappointed. That does not make me ungrateful.

I do not have to suffer through this.

My mental health struggle is valid.

I am allowed to grieve my feeding journey.

Exercise
Challenging Negative Thoughts Toward Feeding

When considering which feeding methods are right for you, it is common to experience negative thoughts if you feel like you're not doing what society says is best for your child or if a majority of the people you know have done it one way. If you run into feeding challenges, you might even view yourself as a bad parent. In order to challenge some of these negative thoughts, go through the following steps and see if you can come up with an alternative way of viewing the situation that supports your mental and emotional well-being. A hypothetical example is provided for you at each step.

Step 1: Identify the thought. Recognize a thought you have about yourself regarding feeding and write it down here**.**

Example: *I have failed as a mother because my child needs to be supplemented by formula.*

_____

_____

_____

_____

_____

_____

Step 2: Describe how this negative thought makes you feel. What are the different emotions you feel when you think or say this to yourself?

Example: *This makes me feel incompetent, worthless, and guilty.*

_____

_____

_____

_____

Step 3: Look at the evidence. What is the evidence to support this thought? Is anyone making you feel bad about your feeding choices? Are you creating this narrative toward yourself?

Example: *Every time I go to the doctor's office, they tell me my child is gaining weight appropriately and is well taken care of. This evidence supports the fact that I am a good mother, despite what I tell myself.*

_____

_____

_____

_____

_____

_____

_____

_____

Step 4: Evaluate the thought. Is this a helpful or an unhelpful thought? Will this thought help or hinder you?

Example: *This thought is unhelpful because when I tell myself that I am a bad mother, it makes me feel disconnected from my baby and makes it harder to bond during feeding times.*

_____

_____

_____

_____

_____

_____

Step 5: Think of alternative perspectives. If you were talking to your best friend, what would you say if they were having this thought?

Example: *Breastfeeding can be hard, and many children need to be supplemented. You are being a good mother by ensuring that your child gets enough nutrients.*

_____

_____

_____

_____

_____

_____

Step 6: Describe how this new perspective makes you feel. What emotions come up when you think of this new thought?

Example: *This new perspective makes me feel at ease, calmer, and more confident. It reminds me that, as a mother, I always try to do what is best for my child.*

_____

_____

_____

_____

_____

_____

Exercise
Flexible Feeding Plan

A flexible feeding plan is an opportunity to explore what options and resources you have access to when it comes to feeding your child. We want you to explore your own personal beliefs around feeding, challenge yourself to explore alternative options, and find ways to feel more prepared should your feeding journey go an unexpected way. We've provided an example of a completed flexible feeding plan first, followed by space for you to fill one out for yourself. If you are working with a trusted health professional, we encourage you to explore this plan with them as well. They may have resources you weren't aware of and can provide you with information that supports your feeding journey.

Which option for feeding feels the best for you right now?

> Breastfeeding

Do you feel like alternatives are an option? Why or why not?

> If I had to choose an alternative option, I feel like combo feeding or pumping would feel better than formula feeding because I want to provide my baby with at least some breastmilk (at least while I am able to).

Who can support you with your feeding method in your family or personal network?

My mom
My friend Sarah (who had to combo feed)
My husband

What supplies do you need to engage in this feeding method?

Burp cloths, nursing bra, breastfeeding pillow, and nipple cream. I would also like to have a breast pump and bottles on hand if I need to switch to an alternative option. I will also research formulas that I'm most comfortable using to combo feed.

What resources in your community can you reach out to if feeding doesn't go as planned?

The public health nurse
The local hospital's breastfeeding clinic
My family doctor
My lactation consultant

Flexible Feeding Plan

Which option for feeding feels the best for you right now?

_____

_____

Do you feel like alternatives are an option? Why or why not?

_____

_____

_____

_____

Who can support you with your feeding method in your family or personal network?

_____

_____

_____

_____

_____

What supplies do you need to engage in this feeding method?

_____

_____

_____

_____

_____

_____

What resources in your community can you reach out to if feeding doesn't go as planned?

_____

_____

_____

_____

_____

_____

TAKEAWAYS

We hope that you found this chapter to be inclusive and supportive of feeding methods, including how they relate to mental health. It is more than okay to choose whatever method is best for you and your child. It is important to know your options, have support in place, and move through your feeding journey as best as you can.

At the end of the day, you get to figure out what works with your family system and to implement those strategies. Sometimes it can feel frustrating when that choice is taken away from you, and you are "forced" into formula or tube feeding. Please know that you aren't alone in that, and we are here for you.

OUR FAVORITE RESOURCES

- The Breastfeeding Dietitian (https://breastfeedingdietitian.com)

- The Formula Mom (https://www.theformulamom.com)

- KellyMom (https://kellymom.com)

- *When Breastfeeding Sucks* by Zainab Yate

5   The Contradiction of Motherhood

Let's be honest: Motherhood is confusing. It's a wild ride, filled with a mixture of (often) conflicting emotions. What do we mean by conflicting? The list is endless: You're excited for your kids to finally go to bed but then look at pictures of them while they sleep. You desire for your children to grow up but are simultaneously sad that they won't be little forever. You want to go out and do things but are overwhelmed at the idea of packing up everything you need for an outing with your child. You love your life with your child but miss the freedoms and identity you had before becoming a parent. You're exhausted and want to get sleep but feel compelled to stay up late to have some time to yourself. Are any (or all) of these sounding familiar?

The Contradiction of Motherhood

I can't wait for bedtime.

I am so exhausted and need to go to bed early.

I want to go out and do things.

I can't imagine my life without my kids.

I miss them.

I am going to stay up late for some "me" time.

It's so much work to get out of the house.

I miss who I used to be before having children and the freedoms that came with it.

Where do all of these contradictions come from? Oftentimes, these contradictory internal messages arise from the expectations that your family, culture, or society place on you. Women are often expected to look, act, parent, and behave in certain ways that are not only unrealistic but also don't align with each other.

For example, women are often given the message that they must do the primary child-rearing while also working or providing for the household in some way. They are also expected to remain emotionally stable, and are told that it is "bad" to show certain emotions like anger. Another example is the societal pressure that women feel to breastfeed their babies, but simultaneously, they are shamed for doing so in public spaces. In some cases, the shame they experience extends beyond just dirty looks. In our small city in Alberta, Canada, a woman was asked to leave a McDonald's by the manager because she was breastfeeding her child. This is not okay.

Given the double-edged pressure that women often receive from society, it should come as no surprise that motherhood itself can involve a mixture of seemingly opposite emotions, such as gratitude versus grief, joy versus sadness, exhaustion versus excitement, anger versus pleasure, and love versus loneliness. Let's take a closer look.

PARENTING ATTITUDES

Social influences hold an incredible weight on the definition of what a parent—and more importantly, a mother—should be. These influences form the general attitudes that parents (and future parents) take toward parental duties and behaviors. In considering the contradiction of motherhood, there are three primary parenting attitudes that contribute to the mindset: essentialism, the belief that parenting is challenging, and child-centered parenting (Rizzo et al., 2013).

Essentialism is the belief that mothers are natural "experts" in child-rearing and that they do it the best. As a result, the mother is viewed as the essential parent in the relationship. And take it from us, both of us are guilty of perpetuating this belief when we've told our partners, "Just let me do it," "I don't have time to explain it to you," or "You won't do it right, so I'll have to redo it anyway."

Another parenting attitude that can lead to these internal contradictions is *the belief that you do not have the capacity to meet the daily demands of parenting.* If women (and parents in general) believe they don't have the resources to manage the tasks of parenting, they can feel underprepared and overwhelmed. You may feel like you're not cut out to be a mother or that you're failing as a parent, especially when everyone else seems to be doing it "right." We have seen this quite often, both in our private practice and online community.

Finally, *child-centered parenting* is the belief that a parent's (and especially a mother's) life should solely revolve around their children. Not surprisingly, when parents feel like they always have to put their children's needs before their own, it becomes hard to function and find joy in life. This should not come as a huge shock. We cannot be all things to our children. Not only is this not feasible, but it's also not healthy.

Even though these parenting attitudes have such a negative effect on maternal well-being, many mothers continue to hold these beliefs because they have become so ingrained in our society. Women have come to internalize these attitudes, causing a disconnect between where they are and where they want to be. They come to believe that mothers should do and be it all, while loving every minute of it and being hyperfocused on their child. This can lead to an increase in stress, depression, and lower levels of life satisfaction. No wonder moms experience burnout!

OUR EXPERIENCES WITH CONTRADICTION

Caitlin

I remember when my daughter was first born, my older son was two-and-a-half years old, and a very busy toddler. I was feeling anxious as my partner went back to work. With a newborn and a toddler by myself, I wondered what my day was going to look like. Much to my surprise, that first day I was alone with them, it was fine—dare I say, even easy? We had a slow, relaxing morning, and when I put them down for a nap in the afternoon, they both slept for three hours! It was glorious. I watched television, rested, and made supper. I remember thinking, Oh man, if every day is like this, I will have no problem! Well, it was short-lived. That was the last day my toddler napped without significant opposition. I remember struggling through the next few days to get them both to sleep, keep the house somewhat in order, and ensure that the whole family was fed. It was so hard. How was one day so easy and the next a day from the depths of hell?

Just then, I had a "welcome to the contradiction of motherhood" moment. I remembered that one day will be amazing, and the next you will want to pull out your hair. That is completely normal. There is nothing wrong with you for counting down the minutes until bedtime or thinking that you don't know how you are going to get through a tough day. As I am writing this, my two kids are up way past their bedtime, which is frustrating. (When did 9:30 p.m. become the new 7:30 p.m.?) However, I hear them giggling and laughing upstairs, and I want to soak in these moments, because I know they won't play like that forever.

Chelsea

Motherhood feels like this constant push-and-pull effect where I'm caught between guilt and gratitude. As I write this, I feel exhausted and frustrated as my son naps on me. It's the fifth night that I have barely had any sleep. I have this longing to just get out of the house alone. I can actually feel it in my body: the frustration, the sadness, the desire to just do things that I used to do with ease. Then the guilt quickly enters into my mind, settling in like a familiar friend, though it is no friend at all: How dare you not be grateful? This voice reminds me of a difficult boss I had many years ago, who once told me, "How dare you not be grateful for this amazing opportunity! Not everyone will get this opportunity." My mind also wanders to people in my life who would have been absolutely amazing parents but did not get the opportunity to have a child. The nagging guilt in my head reminds me that they would have been such better parents than I am. They wouldn't be wishing these moments away. They would have been savoring it all.

However, the reality is that so many parents experience guilt for not loving the journey of parenthood. I remember one of my friends did several rounds of in vitro fertilization to have a baby, and when the baby finally came, she really struggled with not enjoying the newborn stage. I remember her saying, "I cried over this! I spent sleepless nights wondering why I couldn't get pregnant. I resented friends who had their babies easily and rolled my eyes at their struggles. I would think, What are they whining about? At least they have a baby. And here I am, the biggest fraud out there. How dare I not be grateful for this moment?" The conflict was exasperating for her, as it often is for me. Whether you went through five rounds of IVF or got pregnant on the first try, the contradiction of motherhood doesn't discriminate.

YOUR EXPERIENCE WITH CONTRADICTION

Now that we've shared our experiences and talked a little bit about the contradictions of motherhood, see if you feel comfortable taking some time to reflect on the contradictions you've experienced during your journey into parenthood.

What are some contradictory experiences or emotions you've noticed in your parenting role?

_____

_____

_____

_____

_____

_____

What messages have you received from friends, family, or society as a whole that contribute to these contradictions?

_____

_____

_____

_____

_____

_____

Do you agree with any of the messages? Which ones and why?

_____

_____

_____

_____

_____

Do you disagree with any of the messages? Which ones and why?

_____

_____

_____

_____

COPING WITH THE CONTRADICTION

So when you have all of these contradictions and conflicting messages swirling around in your life, what do you do? First and foremost, you need to know that it is completely normal to feel these conflicting emotions. It is normal to want to savor the experience of rocking your baby back and forth—taking in that beautiful newborn smell and relishing in the laughs, the smiles, and the babbling—while simultaneously wanting that stage to hurry up and pass because the crying seems never-ending and you are so physically exhausted that your body and mind hurt.

Some people say, "Oh, it will get easier when they are potty trained/when they sleep through the night/when they are in school/when they are teenagers." But it doesn't necessarily get easier; it just becomes different. Your thoughts, your gratitude, your worries, your stressors, and your annoyances don't disappear; they just shift over time.

Although the contradictions of motherhood can feel constant, it does not mean that you are doing something wrong. The thing about emotions is that they are all valid, even the ones that don't seem so pleasant. Emotions are not bad, and you are not a bad parent for having them. Emotions exist within you for a reason—even the uncomfortable ones—so we encourage you to feel them all. The next time you feel angry, sad, or resentful, see if you can welcome the experience rather than pushing it away. The following pages provide tools and exercises to help you acknowledge and be comfortable with any emotions that may arise related to the puzzling contradiction of motherhood.

Exercise
Affirmations for the Contradiction of Motherhood

Motherhood is tiring, messy, loud, and beautiful. It can cause you to feel the highest of highs, but also the lowest of lows. The next time you feel tempted to push away the experiences of motherhood that don't feel so pleasant, use the following affirmations to remind yourself that it is acceptable to feel *all* the things. In fact, that is the beautiful part of being a parent (and being human). As always, take what works for you, leave what doesn't, and adapt any of the statements to fit your experience better.

It is normal to have two opposing emotions. This makes me human.

I can hold space for both these emotions at the same time.

I can have emotions that aren't always pretty.

Raw emotions are okay.

I can grieve the life I had before kids while celebrating the life I have now.

Angry emotions are okay.

I don't have to love every minute of motherhood to be a good mom.

I can manage, I am capable.

I am where I need to be in life right now.

Exercise
Making Space for Contradictions

When it comes to parenting, we have all heard phrases like "Soak up every minute because it doesn't last long" or "Blink and they will be all grown up before you know it." While these sayings are well meaning for the most part, they ignore the conflicting emotions we can feel as parents. It is normal to simultaneously hold thoughts of "I really do not like this at all" *and* "I love my child so much."

In order to help you make space for the contradictions in your life, circle or put a check mark by any of the following contradictions that resonate with you. There is also space for you to write in any of your own. Whenever you need a reminder that motherhood is one big, amazing contradiction, simply bring out this piece of paper and read through these statements again.

1. Some days I have felt the love and happiness bursting from within me... *Yet other days, I have felt sad and lonely.*

2. I've felt so incredibly connected and passionate toward my partner... *Yet other days, I become filled with resentment and frustration.*

3. Some days I want to soak in every beautiful minute... *But other days, I count down the seconds until I can say goodnight to my kids.*

4. I've never felt more secure in my role as a mother... *Yet I often ask myself, "Is this all there is?"*

5. The strength of my mama bear protective instinct astonishes me beyond belief... *Yet the vulnerability of my babies makes me scared to send them out in the world.*

107

6. Some days I walk around frustrated that I am picking up the same mess again and again... *But other days I look at the toys and clothes they have outgrown and yearn for those moments back.*

7. _____
_____
_____
_____
_____
_____

8. _____
_____
_____
_____
_____
_____

9. _____
_____
_____
_____
_____
_____

10. _____

_____

_____

_____

_____

_____

_____

_____

Exercise
Examining Your Values

As you've learned, women are often expected to do it all and be it all when it comes to parenting. We're expected to have secure jobs, engage in community building, take the brunt of child-rearing, and have a sparkling clean home, all while not feeling stressed out. Who can live up to these expectations? Many of us struggle just to keep our children busy, let alone juggle everything else that life throws at us, yet we continue to internalize these messages that cause us unnecessary conflict and tension. Let's unpack these messages a bit and filter out some of the noise.

What expectations are you currently putting on yourself that make you feel the push and pull of motherhood?

_____

_____

_____

_____

_____

_____

_____

_____

Are these expectations realistic? For example, are you expecting that everything will come naturally? Does everyone else seem to be killing this parenting thing but you?

_____

_____

_____

_____

_____

_____

Would you hold a friend to these same expectations if they were in your shoes? If not, what would you tell them instead?

_____

_____

_____

_____

_____

_____

Often, your expectations for yourself has been internalized from messages you have heard somewhere else. What messages are fueling your expectations, and where do you believe you heard them? Your family, friends, partner, or social media? Are these messages consistent with your values? Why or why not?

_____

_____

_____

_____

_____

_____

_____

_____

_____

TAKEAWAYS

Motherhood is by nature a beautiful contradiction, an amazing push and pull of frustration and joy, grief and gratitude, loneliness and fulfillment. When you realize that this contradiction is normal, it becomes easier to step back and embrace it. You can realize that it is okay to make space for all the emotions that arise. You can be both grateful *and* grieving. Happy *and* sad. Exhausted *and* excited.

Above all, grant yourself the forgiveness to *not* love every aspect of motherhood. (Heck, sometimes it might even make you want to downright scream.) That is okay. There is no right or wrong way to feel. And when you're being bombarded by external messages that are causing these contradictions, remember to reflect on where the message is coming from, and know that it's okay if you don't subscribe to it. You have a choice, Mama.

what if that truck smashes into me?

what if I drop him down the stairs?

what if she falls out of her crib and breaks her neck?

what if I forget him while he is in the bathtub?

why am I having these thoughts right now? why can't I get them out of my head?!

6   Intrusive Thoughts

It may seem like you are the only one in the world who experiences these types of thoughts, but research has shown that you are not! Intrusive thoughts, which are distressing and unwanted thoughts that come out of nowhere, are a universal experience among new mothers. You might be going about your day, enjoying yourself, when all of a sudden—BOOM—you are hit with an intrusive thought. They really can be that random.

In addition to intrusive thoughts (*What if I drop the baby down the stairs?*), you can have intrusive images (seeing your baby submerged underwater). These thoughts and images typically center around the baby's safety, health, and security, and can include thoughts that about doing something accidentally (e.g., falling down the stairs with the baby) or even intentionally (e.g., throwing the baby against the wall). They can feel oh-so-vivid and horrific.

It's important to note that the distress you feel about these thoughts is key. If thoughts of harming your baby are disturbing to you, that is a sign of a normal intrusive thought that is generally not cause for concern. However, if these thoughts are *not* distressing to you—maybe you even find them to be relieving—then it is important to call 911 or to head to your nearest emergency room immediately, as this is a warning sign of postpartum psychosis. (We will dive into this topic in more detail in chapter 15.)

Characteristics of Intrusive Thoughts

Are extremely
common

Can feel scary

Can lead to
feelings of shame
and guilt

Are unconscious
and uncontrollable

Can be memories,
thoughts, or what ifs

Can be occasional
or constant

Can be easily
managed or
overwhelm daily life

Can happen even
if you do not have
a perinatal mood
disorder

CATEGORIES OF INTRUSIVE THOUGHTS

There are several common categories of intrusive thoughts that you might have as a parent:

1. **Accidents or injuries.** Thoughts of your baby or you having an accident. This can include thoughts of dropping the baby, hitting the baby too hard during burping, or forgetting the baby in the car. It can also include thoughts of the baby dying from sudden infant death syndrome (SIDS).

2. **Sickness.** Thoughts of your baby being exposed to harmful germs or contracting an illness. You might have thoughts that your baby will suck on a pacifier or toy covered in bacteria and become sick.

3. **Violence toward yourself or others.** Thoughts of intentionally harming the baby. This can include thoughts of shaking the baby, pushing the stroller into oncoming traffic, or suffocating the baby. We heard from one mom who stated that she hated being around sharp objects because of the intrusive thoughts that would come up.

4. **Sexual.** Thoughts of touching the baby inappropriately (e.g., during diaper changes) or someone else sexually abusing the baby.

Examples of Intrusive Thoughts

What if I drop this knife and cut my baby?

What if my baby drowned in the tub?

What if my baby doesn't wake up?

What if I leave my baby with someone and something bad happens?

What if I drop baby down the stairs?

What if I throw my baby when I'm mad?

I shouldn't have had a baby.

My baby would be better off without me.

It can be very difficult, and even scary, to consider the intrusive thoughts you have experienced. Writing them down might make it even more terrifying, as they can seem more "real" when you see them in front of you instead of in your head. However, it is better to learn to live *with* them than to push them away. Remember that it is normal among new mothers, and we are here to support you.

What are some intrusive thoughts you have experienced as a parent?

_____

_____

_____

_____

_____

WHY AM I HAVING THESE THOUGHTS?

It is important to recognize that just because you are having intrusive thoughts does not mean you have postpartum depression, anxiety, or OCD. In fact, it is extremely common to have intrusive thoughts, even for those without diagnosed mental health disorders or who aren't postpartum mothers. And while it's true that scary thoughts can increase among those with postpartum mental health disorders, they are super common among nearly *all* new mothers (and many partners too!)—having them doesn't mean that anything is wrong with you! But why are you having them?

There are a few different reasons:

1. As a parent, your brain is doing its job by keeping you aware of potential dangers to your child. Have you heard the saying "I'm a parent—it's my job to worry"? There is some literal truth to this.

2. You are stressed and tired beyond belief. Being a parent is exhausting, and when your brain is tired, it's simply harder to access and implement strategies to calm down your body and mind.

3. Have you ever had a new job? If so, you probably doubted yourself and your skills at first—it's likely you didn't know what the heck you were doing those first couple weeks on the job. It's the same with motherhood.

4. You don't have enough social support. Your community may not be as helpful as what you anticipated, perhaps because they live far away or because you are hesitant to reach out for help.

Intrusive thoughts can even make some degree of sense from an evolutionary perspective. When you become a parent, you become responsible for a little human being. This is a huge life change—you have never been responsible for anything so precious before. During pregnancy, you took care of yourself, just like you had done for many years. However, now this tiny, helpless little person is here—a person who relies on you for its every need. As a result, you may become hypervigilant for any potential dangers in your environment.

Historically, this is the same thing your ancestors did: They had to remain vigilant over their surroundings in order to survive; otherwise, wild animals could have literally eaten the baby. So in a super-not-helpful and weird way, intrusive thoughts are a reflection of your brain's biological wiring to keep you (and your kids) out of harm's way. These thoughts prompt you to be on the lookout in protective ways.

WHY ARE THESE THOUGHTS NOT TALKED ABOUT?

Caitlin struggled big time with intrusive thoughts during random times in her life, usually related to a stressor that would come up. (During one particular high-stakes job interview, she even thought, *What if I just told the interviewer to f*ck off?*). These thoughts have always been present to some degree, but they would come and go, and she could generally manage them, shake them off, and continue on with her day.

However, once she had a baby, these thoughts became unleashed like never before. The what-ifs and vivid scenes played out in her mind, and she would judge herself and feel horrible: *What kind of a mother has these thoughts? Why can't I get this out of my head?* It was a vicious cycle. No one told her that these scary thoughts are shared by so many moms. (And she was a therapist with over eight years of schooling behind her at that point!) Even during a prenatal weekend course she took, no one mentioned the likelihood of these thoughts. All 14 people in this class were likely to experience accidental harm intrusive thoughts at some point after their babies were born—but still, nothing was shared.

After a lot of researching and digging, it has become clear that there are so many myths circulating about intrusive thoughts that keep people from talking about them. Let's dispel some of these myths right now:

- **Myth:** You will get your kids taken away if you let anyone know you are having distressing thoughts.

  Fact: It is important to talk to a trusted friend, family member, or health professional if you have intrusive thoughts that trouble you.

By letting others know that you are having these thoughts you are letting them know that you want help. You are not "crazy" or any of the awful derogatory names that get thrown around carelessly. Wanting to receive help for distressing thoughts is not a reason for your children to be taken away.

- **Myth:** You are a bad mom for having these thoughts.

  Fact: You are the best mom for your baby. Your desire to understand more about intrusive thoughts proves that you are a good mom.

- **Myth:** Having these thoughts means you are deeply troubled.

  Fact: Research has shown almost all new moms have thoughts of accidental harm, while 50 percent have thoughts of intentional harm (Collardeau et al., 2019). You are not deeply troubled. This is a common part of motherhood.

- **Myth:** You will act on these thoughts.

  Fact: The fact you are troubled by these thoughts, and that they are incongruent with your character and values, shows that you will not act upon them.

- **Myth:** You secretly want the thoughts to happen.

  Fact: These thoughts are your brain's way of being hypervigilant. Just because you have a thought does not mean you want it to happen.

Much to the relief of so many mothers, having intrusive thoughts does not mean you are crazy. In fact, the further you try to shove these thoughts into the back of your mind, the more isolated you will feel. When you keep your scary thoughts a secret, it is the perfect breeding ground for shame.

MANAGING INTRUSIVE THOUGHTS

Now you might be wondering, *Okay, I have these intrusive thoughts, so how do I tell them to take a hike?* Unfortunately, getting rid of intrusive thoughts isn't as simple as blocking them out of your mind. In fact, when you try to push them out of your mind, they can often come back at you with a vengeance. However, it is possible to develop ways to manage and cope with the thoughts.

Cognitive behavioral therapy (CBT) has been found to be the most effective treatment in remedying intrusive thoughts. When these thoughts come up, you can use the following step-by-step process that borrows from the CBT literature:

1. **Acknowledge the thought.** Take a deep breath and let the thought go through your mind without trying to distract yourself from it. Distraction may help you feel better in the short run, but it won't help you cope with future scary thoughts.

2. **Label it as just a thought.** Tell yourself, "I am having a thought, but it doesn't mean I am going to act on it. It's just a thought. It's okay if these thoughts come up. It does not mean I am going to act on them or that it is going to happen."

3. **Determine the evolutionary benefit of this thought.** What potential danger is it alerting you to?

4. **Ask yourself what this thought says about your values.** Remind yourself that this scary thought doesn't mean anything bad about you. In fact, it likely indicates something positive about your values as a parent.

5. **Share with someone you trust and feel comfortable with.**

The following exercises will help you manage and cope with intrusive thoughts pertaining to motherhood as they arise.

Exercise
Affirmations for Intrusive Thoughts

When unwanted thoughts pop into your mind, it can be tempting to push them away or struggle against them in some way. However, doing so only makes them come on stronger and louder. Instead, use the following affirmations to acknowledge these thoughts without judgment and then let them fade away into the background. As always, take what works for you, leave what doesn't, and adapt any of the statements to fit your own experience better.

I am having a thought. It is just a thought.

This thought is uncomfortable, but I can manage it.

This thought does not say anything about me as a mom.

This thought does not reveal anything about my character.

I am safe. My baby is safe.

Just because I have a thought doesn't make it true.

Thoughts are not actions.

Having a thought doesn't mean that I'll act on it.

These thoughts are very common.

Exercise
Managing Intrusive Thoughts

Use these steps to unpack any intrusive thoughts or images you're having about motherhood and to challenge the meaning behind the thoughts. An example is provided for you at each step, followed by some space for you to write your own answers.

Step 1: Identify the thought and write it down here.

Example: *I am having a thought of dropping my baby off our balcony.*

_____

_____

_____

_____

Step 2: Label it as just a thought.

Example: *This is just a thought. This thought does not mean that I am going to act on it. My thoughts are not always facts.*

_____

_____

_____

_____

_____

Step 3: Describe the evolutionary benefit of this thought.

Example: *It is letting me know of the potential danger of a fall.*

_____

_____

_____

_____

Step 4: Ask yourself what this thought says about your values standpoint.

Example: *I value my baby more than anything and want to protect her.*

_____

_____

_____

_____

Step 5: Consider someone you can connect with to share and process this thought.

Example: *My partner or my best friend*

_____

_____

_____

TAKEAWAYS

Psychoeducation has been proven to lessen the distress associated with intrusive and scary thoughts. That is why we are here for you in this chapter. We want you to know that these distressing thoughts are so incredibly common. You are not "losing it." You are not going crazy. You are not a bad mom. These intrusive thoughts are simply a normal experience among postpartum parents. Although these thoughts can seem really scary in the moment, you can learn to name your thoughts, recognize them as just thoughts, and find relief and joy. This is your motherhood. You deserve to enjoy it.

7 Mental Load of Motherhood

The term *mental load* has become popular in social media over the last few years. This term refers to the invisible burden involved in overseeing, organizing, and planning your life and the lives of others—a burden that typically falls on women's shoulders. It refers to literally *all* the things that we as moms need to keep mental track of: upcoming appointments, new clothing the kids need, chores that need to be completed around the house, lunch kits that need to be packed every morning, groceries that need to be shopped for. We could go and on—the mental load is never-ending.

A few years ago, a meme depicting the mental load of motherhood went viral around Christmas (and it still makes it rounds every holiday season). It included some version of this: "Opening gifts from Mom and Dad while knowing that Dad is going to be just as surprised as you are." How many of you can relate? That's because the load of purchasing and wrapping Christmas gifts is left to whom? Mom.

HOW DOES THE MENTAL LOAD DEVELOP?

The mental load women carry often starts from our early upbringing. Think back to how you were raised. For those of you who lived in a two-parent household, who shouldered the load of the family, made the appointments, prepped the meals, and went to the grocery store?

More often than not, it was your mom. Of course, this is not always the case, as there are some really fantastic dads out there too! But in our patriarchal society, this task tends to fall to mothers most of the time.

In addition, children are very often given toys that encourage this gender-oriented division of labor, as girls are given dolls to take care of and boys are given construction tools to build things with. As a result, kids learn that dads go to work to make money, while moms stay home and look after the family. It is only over the last 50 to 60 years that it has become more commonplace for women to be in the workforce, which is mind-blowing when you think about what a short time period this has really been. When you stop to consider the mental load that comes with being expected to go to work, take care of the household *and* shoulder most of the responsibilities of raising their kids, it is no wonder moms are worn out!

Nevertheless, many women continue to shoulder this load because they feel a sense of deep fulfillment when they provide care for their families (Devault, 1994). They also feel a primary responsibility for the day-to-day running of the household and for helping children manage their emotions (Ciciolla & Luthar, 2019). While this role can feel fulfilling, it can constrain women from other roles within society and result in further gender and class divisions. It can also lower a woman's well-being and relationship satisfaction.

THE DEFAULT PARENT

Nothing highlighted the mental load of motherhood more than the COVID-19 pandemic,. All of a sudden, parents were forced to figure out how to work from home while also juggling the responsibilities of childcare (and, for some, facilitating the change to online schooling). During this time, responsibility for keeping the kids quiet or busy during work hours would often fall to the "default parent," regardless of their work-from-home schedule or needs.

The default parent is exactly what it sounds like: the parent who does most of the household work by default. This burden typically falls on the mother—the person whose life has shifted the most since becoming a parent—though this isn't always the case, of course. To illustrate what the default parent looks like, consider this example: It's Sunday morning, and Caitlin's husband is on the computer updating their latest stock portfolio, while she is sitting at the kitchen table half-working and half-parenting, refereeing the latest fight about toys and fetching snacks for the kids while she writes this chapter. Her husband, who is left alone for the most part, is sitting right by the fridge. The kids literally walk past Dad to come tell Mom that they are hungry. This is what it means to be the default parent.

The subject of the default parent started coming up with our mom friends a few years ago. We heard questions like "Does your partner ever get up with the baby? Mine doesn't—must be nice to sleep through the crying" with responses like "Yeah, he does, but usually it doesn't help, so I just send him back to bed." It became clear to us that the role of the default parent often starts from the moment baby is born, and whether the baby is breastfed or formula fed, the mother typically does most of the feedings. It then evolves from there—shouldering most of the day-to-day work of caring for an infant becomes shouldering most of the day-to-day work with the kids.

To determine if you're the default parent, ask yourself these questions and put a check mark by any that apply to you:

- ☐ Do the kids walk past your partner to ask you something?
- ☐ If there is a birthday or school event, are you the parent always making the arrangements?
- ☐ Are you the parent who gets up with the kids consistently?
- ☐ Are you the parent who is the soother of the emotions?
- ☐ Are you the parent who knows what your kids need for school or daycare?
- ☐ Are you the parent who takes time off work if someone is sick?

If you answered yes to most (or all) of these questions, then congratulations—you are the default parent! We want to emphasize that this does not mean that the non-default parent is not involved. They still play a role in supporting the family and raising children. Instead, it means that the non-default parent's responsibilities are often different and don't involve as many standard and expected responsibilities. But at the end of the day, the default parent often carries most of the mental load. It is heavy and it can be tiring. Let's examine some of the invisible loads that a parent can carry.

THE INVISIBLE LOADS

The Invisible Load of the New Baby

This is a loaded one. (No pun intended.) So much of the transition to motherhood is invisible. Although people see the physical changes that happen (there's no baby and then one day, there's a baby!), there is so much that they do not see. Everything from postpartum bleeding,

Characteristics of the Default Parent

Keeps
everyone
fed

Is planner
of all the
things

Organizes
the home

Is the
preferred
caregiver

Does school
pick-up and
drop-off

Is the
soother
of the
emotions

Gets up at
night with
the kids

Rarely gets
a break

painful tears or incisions that need to heal, breastfeeding or formula-feeding struggles, and hormonal shifts to endless appointments to attend, unannounced visitors, postpartum depression (or anxiety or baby blues), and on top of all of that, the intense sleep deprivation.

The Invisible Load of Birthdays and Special Events

Back in December, Chelsea's husband was tasked with buying "a couple" of Christmas presents for the kids. He ended up coming home with two giant books (that were literally the size of posterboards) and three big gifts for their son (a huge dump truck, a giant tub of Play-Doh—we are still finding bits of Play-Doh in every crevice of the house—and a big toy toolbox filled with tools). But he literally got nothing for their daughter. His reason? He didn't know what to get. Face palm. As kids, we never thought about who was in charge of coordinating every birthday, holiday, or special event. It just happened: cake, food, presents, the whole shebang. But someone had to be responsible for all of it. Think back to whom that person was for you.

The Invisible Load of Carrying the Emotions of the Family

If there is one thing that's true about young kids, it's that they are dysregulated *a lot*. They feel all the big feelings, which are often messy and loud. A few years ago, Caitlin remembers yelling (ironically), "I am so sick of being the only regulated person in this house!" Okay, so maybe at that moment she wasn't the most regulated. But she was tired of juggling everyone's emotions in the house, including her partner's. She was also just *tired*, and had no energy left to give anymore. Being a psychologist, she had the skills needed to calm everyone down in a moment of chaos. (Well, most of the time anyway.) Her husband had more of an authoritarian parenting style—firm rules with no room for rationale—while Caitlin was well-versed in positive parenting, which focuses more on the *why* behind the behaviors children are presenting. Although they had several stand offs about parenting approaches, we are happy to say that he is a recovering authoritarian parent.

Now we want to be transparent here: Even though we are psychologists, does this mean that we are perfect parents? Of course not! We have our days, our frustrations, and our moments where we lose it. We are human. But it's easier when both partners work *together* to take on the brunt of the big feelings.

HOW TO OFFSET SOME OF THE LOAD

If you're struggling with the mental load of motherhood, the most important thing you can do to offset your load is to share with your partner how you are feeling. Describe what's included in your invisible load and discuss how you can work together as a team to manage all these responsibilities. Here are ways to get your partner to shoulder more of the emotional load:

- If you're an expectant or new mother, get your partner involved from day one. (And even if you're well past day one, it is never too late to start.)

- Avoid the urge to jump in if your partner is not doing something your preferred way. (It will get done even if it isn't the way you'd do it.) Anything they are doing is something off your plate!

- Notice what your partner is doing that is helpful and communicate this to them! One of the biggest things we see with clients (and even with ourselves) is that their partners tend to take a step back because they feel like they either won't do it the "right" way or they are so used to us taking over that they simply do not take the initiative.

Sometimes putting these steps into practice is easier said than done. That's because negative thoughts often get in the way of your ability to share your invisible load with others. You might think:

- "I'll probably just have to do it over because it won't be done the right way."

- "I shouldn't have to ask for help."
- "It is just easier if I do it myself."
- "I don't trust anyone but myself."
- "I should be able to handle it."

If this sounds like you, then a big chunk of offsetting your load is accepting the fact that you absolutely do need (and deserve) help. Here are some mama mantras you can try repeating to yourself to remind you that this mental load doesn't always need to fall on you:

- "My partner is doing the best job they can."
- "No one is perfect."
- "I want progress, not perfection."
- "I deserve to have help too."

But what if you simply don't have anyone to help you shoulder this invisible load? How do you offset it? We see you mamas: those who simply don't have a partner (or a supportive partner) or whose partner works away from home. You may live away from family or may not have a relationship with your family. For these moms, we cannot understate the importance of finding your village. And this village will look different for everyone. It can be anyone from mom friends to neighbors to your child's teacher. You will be surprised whom you can find support from once you ask for it. There are even different local Facebook groups for moms, and often a mom just has to post that she is looking for help (whether it's regarding childcare, getting groceries, etc.) and she'll get a handful of replies from other parents offering to help. Who knows? You may even find friendships with others who can offer emotional support as well.

To help you figure out how to share your load, first describe the invisible load you carry, such as organizing the household, managing the budget, grocery shopping, planning the milestone events, shopping for clothes, making (and attending) appointments, and so on.

_____

_____

_____

_____

_____

Next, think of how you can offset this load. What can you delegate to your partner? Or, if you're a single parent, whom could you enlist as a support person when things get tough?

_____

_____

_____

_____

_____

MANAGING IT ALL WHEN IT FEELS SO UNMANAGEABLE

As mothers, our brains can feel like a web browser with at least 10 tabs open at any given time. But as we're constantly being interrupted, we keep all these tabs open indefinitely to return to at a later time. If we continue to keep these tabs open (instead of closing everything out and shutting down the proverbial computer that is our brain), then we are inevitably going to hit a wall. And if we burn out, *all* the tabs are going to crash.

So what should you do when you have all the things to do but only one of you to do it? Here's what we recommend.

1. **Schedule your day, week, and month.** We are huge fans of containment, one of the skills we talked about in the chapter on birth trauma—simply writing out a list on paper (or your phone) will help *contain* all the things you need to do so they take up less time and space in your head. Every night before you get ready for bed, write your to-do lists for the next day. Likewise, each week (we do this on Sunday nights), make your weekly to-do list, which can be helpful in prioritizing the tasks that *need* to get done versus those that you *want* to get done. Make sure these tasks are realistic—you don't want to write down a bunch of things that you cannot realistically accomplish. Finally, do this same thing at the beginning of every month, where you can separate tasks into "needs" versus "wants" for the month ahead.

2. **Manage your time suckers.** If social media isn't a huge time sucker, we don't know what is. It is easy to get lost mindlessly scrolling through the internet for hours on end. We even have friends who quit

social media for a while and noticed an improvement in their mental health. However, social media is definitely not the only time sucker. A timer sucker is anything that interferes with your productivity and gets you off track. This can include responding to non-urgent emails, taking too many breaks, wasting time on busy work, or multitasking.

What are your time suckers?

_____

_____

_____

_____

If you mentioned multitasking as one of your main time suckers, you are not alone. Multitasking is a necessary evil for so many parents because there is literally not enough time in the day to get everything done. But anyone who has tried to multitask with kids knows exactly how that turns out: not well. You might be getting your work done in fragmented sessions, with 10 minutes here while the kids are eating, and 20 minutes there while the kids are watching *CoComelon*. While this isn't optimal, it's sometimes the only choice you have after parenting all day long. (Especially for single parents—you are true warriors.)

What we have found helpful in managing time suckers is something called *mindful chunking*. In this technique, you chunk out a section of time for one specific task and then devote your full attention to that specific task for the allotted time. Instead of trying to multitask and do three things at once, you identify blocks of time during which you can dedicate yourself solely to the task at hand. You can reserve several blocks of time per day, but you should only focus on *one* task per "chunk." For example, you might set aside 15 minutes to play with your kids. This chunk is where you are fully engaged and immersed with your kids—down on the floor playing instead of watching from the couch or your computer. Then you chunk another 20 to 30 minutes of mindful time to devote to work. In this chunk, you are not opening your phone, checking emails, browsing through social media, or going down the internet black hole—you are solely doing your work.

What are some tasks or time slots where you could practice mindful chunking?

_____

_____

_____

_____

3. **Set boundaries with social media.** We'll be honest: We are feeling a bit hypocritical right now. Social media is a tricky thing for us because it is technically a part of our job. However, people with *any* type of job may have trouble setting boundaries with social media—their phone is usually within arm's reach the entire day. The seemingly endless feeds on multiple platforms can quickly take time away from everything

else you need to get done. It can be helpful to have set periods of time where your phone is not so easily accessible. For instance, you might put your phone in the other room, lock it in a drawer at your desk, or simply turn it off.

You should also make it a point to only follow accounts that align with your values. The number of like-minded accounts that exist online is overwhelming and, each time you look at your feed, you are being constantly delivered an information overload. You may feel bombarded with constant messages of "do this, not that" when it comes to parenting, and many of the portrayals of parents and motherhood can cause you to fall into the comparison trap. If we feel overwhelmed as clinicians, we can only imagine how other parents feel. For this reason, you should only follow accounts because you *want* to see the content, not because you feel obligated to.

What are one or two parenting accounts that you find value in?

_____

_____

4. **Set boundaries with your kids.** Some of you might read this heading and think, *Can I even do that?* Yes! You can set boundaries with your kids and still be a good parent. You don't have to engage with them every waking moment. It is okay to set boundaries around your needs or your limits. For example, let's say that you're busy working, and your child keeps whining about wanting to play with you ("*Mommm, can you play with me? Mom please, Mom please!*"). To set boundaries,

you can say, "You really want me to play, I hear you. Right now, I have to do work stuff, and in 30 minutes I can play with you." Then set a timer and hold the boundary. (Remember, your child is allowed to be upset when you set boundaries, but it is your job to hold that boundary.)

To help you more easily enforce these boundaries, it can be helpful to teach your child independent play habits so they don't always need you to entertain them. One way to set your child up for success is to have a few open-ended toys placed out in the room that they can rotate through. Open-ended toys are those that can be used in a variety of ways, such as kinetic sand, building blocks, magnetic tiles, stuffed animals, or toy vehicles. Because there is no set way to play with open-ended toys, they inspire learning, curiosity, and creativity. To begin, set a timer for one minute (or up to five minutes if your child is a little older) and then gradually increase the amount of independent play your child can enjoy in a single setting. With time, you'll find that your child will be able to happily play on their own, making it easy for you to set boundaries and get things done when you need to.

What are some activities you can use to encourage your child to play independently?

_____

_____

_____

_____

5. **Ask for help.** You may have a hard time asking for help because you think you can, or must, do it all. But the reality is you simply cannot. In order to offload some of your burdens, it's important to get into the habit of asking for two different types of help: *anticipation help* and *in-the-moment help.* Anticipation help involves forecasting and planning for the future. For example, if you know that you have a busy morning coming up, make a point to ask for help beforehand. In contrast, in-the-moment help involves noticing when you are starting to feel overwhelmed and asking for help right then and there, before you reach the point of explosion. Chelsea previously shared about her struggles with this, as she would often let herself get to a boiling point before asking for help. (At that point, it wasn't so much asking for help. It was more yelling about how she had to do everything.) It can be helpful to practice getting into the habit of asking for help.

What are some high-risk situations where you are likely to start feeling overwhelmed?

_____

_____

_____

_____

_____

_____

Then make a plan for who and how you can ask for help in these situations. For example, you might ask your partner: *"I need you to watch the baby while I am getting Olivia ready. Thank you."*

Who I will ask for help:

_____

_____

_____

How I will ask for help:

_____

_____

_____

_____

TAKEAWAYS

The load that you are shouldering is enormous. When you're the one tasked with keeping track of everything, it's not just tiring, it's downright exhausting. Please know that we see how much you are sacrificing out of love for your family. But remember that you need to take care of yourself too. The load of constantly managing it all and neglecting your own needs for the well-being of others can lead to burnout, causing all of your mental tabs to crash. Use the strategies in this chapter to help you offload some of that burden. Life is hard at this moment, and you deserve some grace and compassion.

8   Mom Burnout

Sarah is making dinner in the kitchen while her kids are in the living room fighting. Wooden blocks are flying. Screams are erupting. But Sarah continues to stand at the stove, stirring the pasta. That's because Sarah is completely numb right now and feels like she's hit a brick wall. She couldn't care less about the fighting or about the dinner she is cooking. She is just mindlessly standing in front of the stove, stirring the pasta. The kids continue to fight, the pasta continues to boil, and she continues to stare into the pot. Before it got to this point, Sarah would have jumped in and played referee with her kids, and when everything had settled, she would have returned to what she was doing. But now, Sarah moves through the evening like a robot, completely void of feeling anything.

Joanna, who has a 4-year-old and a 2-year-old, has been a stay-at-home mom for a couple of years now. Given the astronomical cost of childcare in their city, staying at home made the most sense financially. Plus, staying home with the kids was a parenting value of hers. But ever since she left her career, the days seem to simultaneously fly by and drag on. The crying, fighting, and screaming never seem to stop. She finds that she either gives in to her kids or turns into a "momster" who screams and throws things (just like her kids). Either way, Joanna is filled with shame afterward and wants to hide. She hates the person she has become and lies in bed every night with tears running down her face. She has no idea how she is going to make it through another day.

Although these two moms are both dealing with burnout, their experiences are so different. That's because what burnout looks like for one mom can look completely different for another. But that doesn't make either experience any less valid. In this chapter, we're going to take a deep dive into what burnout look likes, discuss some of the causes, and provide you with some remedies that can help.

WHAT IS BURNOUT?

Burnout is the feeling of being disconnected, physically exhausted, and ineffective in your role. This can happen when you are stretched too thin, constantly giving and giving, without any time or space for yourself. Parents are most at risk for burnout when they don't have the adequate resources to meet the demands of parenting. Even if resources are available, they may be hesitant to reach out and admit they are struggling.

As a parent, you might be wondering, *Am I burned out? I'm definitely exhausted, but how do I know if I am burned out or just tired?* At its core, burnout isn't just about "not feeling like yourself" for a day. Here are some signs of burnout. Put a check mark by any that apply to you:

- ☐ You lack energy.
- ☐ It feels like you are dragging yourself from task to task.
- ☐ You feel hopeless that things will get better.
- ☐ You have difficulty acknowledging your emotions.
- ☐ You're quick to anger.
- ☐ You are feeling shame.
- ☐ Doing something for yourself feels impossible.
- ☐ You have no interest in being intimate with your partner.

☐ You look forward to the end of the night where you can numb yourself through drinking.

☐ You have no energy for conversations with friends and family.

☐ You feel like you can't muster up the energy to be engaged with your children.

If you checked off several items on this list, you may be suffering from a case of parental burnout. We are glad you have turned to this chapter. We are going to give you practical, easy-to-implement strategies to help you get back to feeling like yourself.

What Burnout Can Look Like

Easily triggered

Doing something for yourself seems impossible

Overwhelmed by your own emotions

Low motivation for daily activities

Difficulty acknowledging how you feel

Increased anxiety

Exhaustion

Feelings of shame and guilt

WHAT FUELS BURNOUT?

There are a variety of factors that contribute to burnout, but one of the biggest is your sense of what an ideal parent should be. From a very young age, you have created and molded an image in your mind of this ideal parent. This "ideal parent memory bank" holds every little belief and expectation (realistic or not) about motherhood. These beliefs and expectations can come from a variety of places. It may come from a mom in a Mommy and Me group who always seems to have all her shit together. Or it may come from a social media influencer who always seems to coordinate her family in perfect matching outfits. It may even come from the image you hold of your own mother and how much she did for you as a child.

Regardless of where these images come from, they paint a picture in your mind of what everything should look like: what your house should look like, how you should dress, and what activities your kids should be doing. And don't even get us started about the messages we get about needing to prep children for a "perfect" future. There is this idea that if you don't do every little thing to prop your child up for success (enroll them in every extracurricular activity, have an activity ready to go during quiet time, or—heaven forbid—let them have a little extra screen time or processed food), then they will not succeed in life. Yikes! Once this hamster wheel starts spinning, it can be tricky to jump off.

Many of these idealized pressures have been intensified by the idea of *positive parenting*, which has become a buzz phrase across social media and is touted by many parents as an ideal to strive for. Don't get us wrong, positive parenting is a great thing. In fact, we talk about it on our Instagram page as a way to acknowledge, hear, and accept children's feelings. However, for some parents, the concept of positive parenting can lead to the desire to be the "perfect positive parent"—an ideal that is unrealistic to live up to. You want to do it all and have it all together perfectly. However, perfectionism is a recipe for burnout because you simply cannot do it all and do it well.

Characteristics of Perfectionist Parents

Have overwhelming feelings of guilt and shame

Have difficulty asking for help

Are highly self-critical

Experience high anxiety

Constantly compare yourself to others

Often question your success as a parent

Want to do it alone

Are emotionally and physically exhausted

SENSORY OVERLOAD IN PARENTING

Another area that can contribute to burnout is the amount of sensory overload in your life. Some people are relatively unbothered by sensory stimulation, while others struggle with it. But let us tell you, nothing will overstimulate your senses like #momlife.

Before you became a parent, you probably had a good amount of control over the sensory input in your life. You could decide if you wanted to eat in a noisy restaurant, shop at a crowded mall, or put a time limit on (or even completely avoid) other activities that gave you sensory overload. However, after becoming a parent, sensory overload becomes inevitable. There is so much noise. *All the time.* This can make it hard to find time for yourself when there are multiple sensory stressors getting thrown at you from every direction. These stressors can come in the form of a crying baby, a cluttered house filled with toys, or a nagging toddler who won't leave you alone for more than two minutes. How many of you try to have a conversation only to be drowned out by a noisy toy or interrupted by one of your kids?

In addition, we've heard from so many parents who have told us, "I am so touched out." Whether you've been breastfeeding your baby nonstop or have had toddlers crawling over you all day long, it can make you want to repel your partner when they come in for a hug (or more). All you're thinking in those moments is *No! I don't want to be touched!* This can create feelings of guilt and frustration for both parties, but it's another sign of sensory overload.

If excessive sensory stimulation is contributing to burnout, here are some steps you can follow to cope with the sensory overload.

Step 1: Name and acknowledge what you are experiencing: "I am feeling way too much noise coming into my space. This is feeling overwhelming." One way to determine whether you're experiencing sensory overload is to tune in to how your body is feeling. For instance, you may notice more tension and tightness in your chest and stomach. Perhaps you'll have the urge to get away from others and the feeling of being very irritated and edgy.

What are your signals of sensory overload? Where do you feel it in your body?

_____

_____

_____

_____

_____

Step 2: Identify your triggers. What type of sensory stimulation pushes your buttons? For example, Caitlin's son has this Paw Patrol toy that he plays with in circles on the floor. It is so loud that she swears she can feel it vibrating in her soul. The noise makes it really hard to think or even carry on a conversation. But by identifying your triggers ahead of time, you can prep in advance for sensory situations that send you teetering over the edge.

What are your triggers? What sensory stimulation is hard for you to handle?

_____

_____

_____

Step 3: Whenever you find yourself in the presence of one of these triggers, step out of the room for a moment instead of trying to push through it. Even if you have a young baby, put them in their crib, bassinet, or somewhere else that is safe. You want to create small moments of sensory deprivation in your day where you can gather your thoughts, take a breath, and find a break from the loudness of it all. For moms with young kids who have an uncanny ability to track you down and find you, these quiet moments are fleeting. Often, the only place where you can get some quiet solitude is the bathroom. That's fine! Do what you have to do to take that time for yourself, to get a few quiet moments without the constant noise. (Caitlin now understands why her mom always kept books in the bathroom when she was growing up.)

Where can you go to find moments of quiet and stillness, even for just a few minutes? What can you do here to find some calm?

_____

_____

_____

REMEDIES FOR BURNOUT

When looking to treat burnout, start with the notion of self-compassion. At its core, self-compassion involves being warm and kind with yourself in times of failure or difficulty. When you practice self-compassion, you treat yourself the same way you would treat a good friend or small child. Dr. Kristin Neff (2009), a longtime self-compassion researcher, has found that three common elements make up the concept of self-compassion:

1. **Self-kindness.** When you practice self-compassion, you are kind and gentle with yourself in moments of suffering rather than being harsh, judgmental, and critical.

2. **Common humanity.** Self-compassion involves the recognition that everyone in the world has experienced hurt and suffering. You are not alone in your experience of hardship and pain.

3. **Mindfulness.** Self-compassion also involves being able to observe difficult thoughts and emotions without becoming consumed by them. Acknowledge and validate their existence while also recognizing that hard things are often no one's fault; sometimes things in life are just hard.

Although self-compassion is easy to say, it's hard to implement in practice. That's because so many of us struggle with the notion of being kind to ourselves. We fall into the habit of attacking ourselves with self-criticism and blame when we believe we have failed. But can you imagine if you spoke aloud the critical words that you say to yourself? What about saying them to someone you love? Most people cannot imagine having these hurtful words leave their lips, let alone saying them to someone they care about.

So how do you get into the habit of self-compassion? The next time you make a mistake, experience a setback, or feel like you're struggling in some way, try these three steps:

1. **Take inventory of your self-talk.** Are you treating yourself with understanding, or are you berating yourself? Would you speak to a good friend or child like this? If not, what would you say to them?

2. **Remember that you are human.** Being a human is hard sometimes, and you are allowed to feel hard feelings—everyone else feels them too. You can move through hard emotions.

3. **Acknowledge that you are having a tough time.** "This is a tough moment. I am allowed to have all these feelings. I am allowed to make mistakes and have difficult and imperfect moments. All my emotions are valid."

We also encourage you to give the following exercise a try to cultivate a little more self-compassion in your life.

Exercise
Cultivating Self-Compassion

Reflect on a tough moment you had today. Maybe the baby was crying all day, you yelled at your partner, or you got a poor performance review at work. Write down whatever tough moment comes to mind. Then describe any critical self-talk you had, how this made you feel, and what you might say instead to a loved one.

What was the toughest moment of the day?

_____

_____

_____

_____

_____

What harsh criticisms did you have for yourself?

_____

_____

_____

_____

_____

_____

What did you feel in your body? What physical sensations came up?

_____

_____

_____

_____

What would you say to your child or best friend if they were experiencing this tough situation?

_____

_____

_____

_____

What would it feel like to speak to yourself in this new way?

_____

_____

_____

_____

ADDITIONAL REMEDIES FOR BURNOUT

Set Boundaries

In addition to practicing self-compassion, there are a variety of other tools that are important for combatting burnout. The first tool involves boundaries. Set firm boundaries and don't apologize for setting them. You're setting these limitations to protect yourself, and it's not your job to convince anyone else that they are necessary or helpful. The only thing you can control is how you set the boundary, not how others react to it. You can find more information on boundary setting in chapter 3.

Lower the Bar

If you struggle with perfectionism, know that while it is okay to set a high bar in some areas of your life, you cannot devote 100 percent of yourself to every single area, all the time. It is unrealistic to spend quality time playing with your kids, have a sparkling house, cook a homemade supper, and create homemade Valentine's Day cards all in one night. Sure, you can try to do it all, but something is going to fall to the wayside. To keep yourself from burning out, you need to ask yourself where you can lower the bar and still feel okay.

In what areas of your life do you feel that it's necessary to keep your high standards?

_____

_____

_____

In what areas do you feel comfortable lowering the bar, even just a little bit? What can you let go of?

_____

_____

_____

Practice Mindfulness

The word *mindfulness* has been thrown around a lot in recent years, but what does it even mean? Mindfulness simply involves being aware of the present moment instead of dwelling on the past or worrying about the future. When you are mindful, you focus on living in the "here and now."

Mindfulness is something that Caitlin has always struggled with, as her busy brain always has a million tabs open at once. For as long as she can remember, she has always worked two to three jobs simultaneously. She could schedule, overschedule, and sleep in bits and chunks here and there with no problem. Sure, she was tired, but it was nothing a ton of caffeine or a long nap on the weekend couldn't fix! However, becoming a parent was a whole different ballgame. Her workload began to pile up, and her lack of an effective time management method showed flaws in her system. Chelsea would literally think of all the tasks she needed to do, but she would still spend her time checking email or scrolling through social media and get absolutely nothing done. Her brain was on overdrive, and her anxiety paralyzed her to the point of indecision. She was on edge all the time and felt ineffective in her role at work and as a parent.

Something had to change, so she started implementing mindful moments throughout the day. Instead of attempting to multitask, she practiced being fully present in one area at a time. This helped interrupt the vicious cycle in which she would play with her kids (only to feel frustrated that her work was not getting done) or try to work (only to still "half play" with the kids).

In addition to taking a mindful moment, there are a variety of mindfulness exercises that you can try if you're feeling burned out. Mindfulness can reduce burnout by allowing you to connect with your body and mind. When you are more aware of your internal experiences, you can better attune to your stress level and be proactive in lowering that stress level. Can you think of a time when you felt tension in your body after a particularly challenging day? It is likely that your body was starting to feel the effects of stress before you were even aware of it. By being mindful of your internal experiences, you can begin to react to stress before it gets too overwhelming. Let's explore a few mindfulness exercises that you might find helpful.

Exercise
Take a Mindful 5

The following is a combination of a mindfulness and gratitude exercise, which can help you combat the effects of burnout by reminding you of what you are grateful for in life. This can bring you a sense of calm, peace, and ease. Practice this exercise a few times a week. Stop, take a moment, and just notice.

Name five people you deeply care for.

_____

_____

_____

_____

_____

Name four smells that evoke good memories.

_____

_____

_____

_____

Name three things you like to taste.

_____

_____

_____

Name two places where you feel a sense of peace.

_____

_____

Name one thing that is going well.

_____

_____

_____

_____

Exercise
Body Scan

Doing a body scan is a wonderful way to bring attention to the different sensations and feelings in your body, which can increase your ability to be mindful of feelings as they arise rather than pushing them down, ignoring them, or becoming overwhelmed by them.

To begin, find a comfortable place to sit or lie down. You might also find it helpful to play some relaxing music or quiet nature sounds—whatever feels soothing to you. Then close your eyes and begin taking some slow and gentle breaths. As you breathe in and out, start focusing your attention to the sensations in the bottoms of your feet. You just want to notice the sensations without judging or labeling them. These sensations are neither good nor bad; they are just sensations.

Spend a few moments noticing and breathing into the sensations in your feet, then continue this same practice with other areas of your body, gradually working your way up through your calves, upper legs, buttocks, lower back, stomach, upper back, chest, shoulders and neck, until you reach the top of your head.

Then repeat again, starting from the top of your body and working your way down.

Exercise
Mindful Walk

The purpose of taking a mindful walk is twofold. Not only does moving your body get the feel-good hormones going, but it also increases your ability to stay grounded in the present moment. During moments of stress and unease, the benefits of mindful walking can help prevent you from spiraling into burnout.

To begin, step outside and focus your awareness on all the sounds, sights, and smells that surround you. Begin walking, and as you move, notice the sounds and sensations of each step. Notice the sensation your shoe makes as it hits the ground, as well as the sound of any crunching leaves or brushing of grass as you move along your path. See if you can bring attention to the different sensations in your feet as you navigate different terrain, perhaps noticing how it feels to walk on the various bumps or grooves in the ground.

As you walk, continue to notice the sounds around you, including those that are close by and those in the distance. Then switch your focus to any sights that capture your attention, observing any vivid colors or objects in your field of vision. Finally, see if you can notice any smells in your surroundings, such as the scent of wet grass or freshly planted flowers.

To complete this exercise, bring your attention back to the sensations in your feet as they hit the ground.

Make Time to Fill Your Own Bucket

Last, but certainly not least, when it comes to addressing the effects of burnout, you need to take time for yourself. We cannot emphasize this enough! And we know this is damn hard sometimes. Many of you are single parents, parents without a supportive partner, or parents without a solid support system. But you still need time away from the demands of parenthood—the noise, the chaos, and the feeling of being pulled in multiple directions.

Take some time to find your network—that group of people you can text when you are at the end of your rope, even if you're just sending them a bunch of GIFs or having a vent session about how frustrating some things are. We are just finishing up a therapy group for postpartum moms, which consists of 10 moms from different places. These moms, who were strangers when we started, have connected on such a deep, intimate level that it gives us goosebumps. We cannot understate the power of feeling safe, empowered, and supported.

In addition, explore different self-care strategies that work for you. Notice what makes you feel more relaxed and regulated, as well as what doesn't really do it for you. We are all so different, and what relaxes us is going to differ as well. Taking a walk around the block or watching a crime documentary may not be the go-to strategy for everyone. You don't want self-care to feel as though it is a chore—this defeats the purpose. You want it to be something that you look forward to and are motivated to engage in.

SELF-CARE IDEAS

Here are some different self-care ideas to fill your bucket, depending on how much free time you have, as well as some space for you to brainstorm your own ideas. Put a check mark by any ideas that stand out to you.

Self-care when you have 5 minutes (or when you have no idea when the baby is going to wake up):

- Eat a favorite snack
- Listen to a brief guided visualization
- Sit in the sun
- Name three things you are grateful for
- Do some coloring or sketching
- Stretch your body
- Take deep breaths
- Wash your face
- _____
- _____

Self-care when you have 10 minutes:

- Make a cup of tea or coffee
- Lie down with your eyes closed and visualize your calm place (from chapter 1)

- Sit under a weighted blanket
- Run a bath for your feet and sit with your feet in hot water
- Stand outside and notice five different things
- Tighten and relax your muscles
- Light a candle and take in deep breaths
- _____
- _____

Self-care when you have 20–30 minutes:

- Shower
- Make tea or coffee and put on your favorite comedy
- Read a chapter in a book
- Go for a walk around the block
- Go to your room and lie down with a weighted blanket
- _____
- _____

Self-care when you have an hour:

- Watch a show or documentary
- Take a workout class and stretch afterward
- Read a few chapters in a book
- Take a bath

- Put together a puzzle
- Listen to music

- _____

- _____

Self-care when you have half a day or more!

- Go for a drive
- Go window shopping or actual shopping
- Go to the mall and people watch
- Go for a drive to the next town
- Go out to breakfast by yourself, smile, and offer a helping hand to the mom struggling with young kiddos

- _____

- _____

TAKEAWAYS

We see all you parents out there: struggling with the never-ending to-do list, feeling like you're reliving the same day over and over again, wondering how you are going to find time for yourself. We also know that caring for yourself is easier said than done. If you take away anything from this chapter, we hope that it's easier for you to spot your burnout symptoms and that you found a couple of strategies that might help. Start small, keep it simple, and add one thing into your day or week as you can.

I shouldn't have yelled.

I should have set firmer boundaries.

I shouldn't have fed them fast food.

I snapped again.

They watched too much TV.

I gave in to their tantrums.

I worked too much today.

I was on my phone too much today.

I did not read to them today.

I forgot to brush their teeth.

9 Mom Guilt

For many of us, mom guilt is a constant battle in our minds. The list is literally endless. And often, this guilt will stay with us and replay in our heads long after the day is done.

It's easy to feel guilty all the time when every parenting book out there preaches the importance of healthy relationships to a child's development. While safe, loving relationships are incredibly important, imagine how mothers feel when they've just yelled or lost their patience with the kids: "I am such a horrible mom. Who still yells at their kids after reading a pile of positive parenting books?!" These thoughts can make many mothers feel like they're failing at the role of motherhood.

It's no wonder that questions about mom guilt flood our inbox all the time. Many of you want to know where it comes from, why it is so uncomfortable, and how to relieve it. Mom guilt is real, and in this chapter, we'll explore all your questions and more.

MOTHER BLAME

Mom guilt is rooted in the idea that the mother is ultimately responsible (or to blame) for what happens with her children, including how they are dressed, how they behave, how much they sleep, how well they eat, and more. The list goes on and on. When a child presents with any type of behavior or concern that seems even remotely undesirable, it is often linked back to the mother's parenting style—either what she did too much of or what she didn't do enough of. Mother blame has largely been driven by society and, to some extent, the health care system,

Mom Guilt Can Make You Wonder...

Am I spending enough time with my kids?

Will I ever be enough?

Am I enough for my kids?

Why can other moms do more than I can?

Am I always making the wrong choices?

Why can't I do it all?

Should I be better?

How do I feel confident as a mom?

as mothers have been historically blamed for causing schizophrenia, autism, and developmental delays in their children. This notion has now been debunked, but the negative associations of what a mom does or does not do continue to live on. Several years ago, the talk show host Dr. Phil even had two whole episodes that pitted stay-at-home moms against working moms in an attempt to conclude which one was better. We wish we were joking!

Paula Caplan (2000), a prolific author and psychologist, originally dove into the concept of mother blame. She put forth the idea that if a mother does not live up to the following four myths, she is ripe for blame by society:

1. Mothers don't get angry.

2. Mothers should naturally know how to raise their children.

3. Mothers should continuously provide endless nurturance.

4. A good mother should have a perfect daughter.

We can see by the word choice—naturally, continuously, perfect—that these are nearly impossible standards to live by. All they claim is that mothers know *exactly* how to raise children from the moment of birth and are able to do it without struggle. These myths do absolutely nothing to serve mothers, but they continue to remain alive and prevalent in our society today. Just take a look at the "mommy shaming" that occurs on social media whenever someone shares any aspect of their parenting life that has gone wrong. The comments sections of these posts are often filled with hateful backlash like "If only she was more careful" or "How could she not notice what was happening?"

In contrast to mother blame is the concept of the "good enough mother," coined by British pediatrician and psychoanalyst Donald Winnicott. According to Winnicott (1953), a "good enough" mother starts off by being very attentive to her newborn child, responding to its every cry of hunger, discomfort, or distress. However, as the child grows, this mother stops responding to every cue with such immediacy. She may miss some cries and simply not have the time or energy to give her child attention 24/7. Importantly, though, this is *not* a bad thing. The world is certainly not a perfect place, and by allowing children to experience the frustration of not always having things go their way, they are better prepared to encounter similar experiences in the real world.

Therefore, in those moments when you fall into the comparison trap and tell yourself that you are not enough, remind yourself that children actually benefit from having an imperfect parent who does not respond to their each and every whim. There is also no such thing as the perfect parent. The reality is that *you* are the best mother for your child.

SHAME VS. GUILT

In Western society, mom guilt is often rooted in shame. So often, when you act in a way that isn't aligned with your values, such as yelling at your kids, you don't just view your behavior as wrong ("Yelling at my kids was not the right way to handle this.")—you also view *yourself* as wrong ("I'm a horrible mother for yelling at my kids."). That's where the difference between guilt and shame lies. Whereas guilt involves the awareness that you *did* something bad, shame involves the belief that *you* are bad.

Guilt can be a useful emotion because it prompts you to correct your wrongdoings and take ownership of your actions. When you've done something wrong, such as yelling at your kids, guilt alerts you of the need to apologize for your behavior and behave differently next time. It reminds you to treat others with the same kindness and respect that you hope to receive in turn. This is what is known as *healthy guilt*.

Sometimes, though, guilt can arise in response to unrealistic standards or expectations that you set for yourself. You may blame yourself for things that are not your responsibility or that you have no control over. This is known as *unhealthy guilt*, or guilt that doesn't need to be there. For instance, let's say a family member gets upset with you for setting healthy boundaries with them, and you start feeling guilty because they're angry with you. This is an example of unhealthy guilt because it's not up to you to control how they're feeling. Your job is to set the boundary; how they react is on them.

Oftentimes, unhealthy guilt can lead you toward shame. A decision you have made is no longer just a decision but a testament to your character. You begin to think that something is flawed, worthless, or broken about you as a person. For example, you might think, *I am a horrible person for setting this boundary.* Shame sucks all the power out of you and makes you want to run away and hide. It is the feeling that takes all the wind out of your sails, making you feel stuck and disconnected.

Highlighting the difference between these two similar, but different, emotions is so important in combatting mom guilt. Although we all experience shame—it is a universal emotion—it is oh-so-present in parenting and motherhood. Consequently, overcoming mom guilt often involves overcoming shame.

Notice what sensations come up in your body when you read about shame. Do you notice any feelings arise, like a tightness in your chest or butterflies in your stomach?

_____

_____

_____

_____

WHAT TRIGGERS US INTO SHAME MODE?

Expectations

Before you became a parent, you likely had a set of values that you *thought* you would abide by when you finally had children. Some of these values might have been very idealistic and, as it turned out, difficult to uphold once you actually begin to raise your child. That's because values tend to shift throughout the years, and ideas that you thought were important before you had children may not be so important now. Remember when you said you would never let your children have a tantrum in public? Or have screen time at a restaurant? Let's all pause for a moment and have a collective laugh together. It is okay to have high expectations, but we also need to evaluate how realistic those expectations are.

It is also important to examine whose expectations these are. Are these the expectations of your friends, colleagues, partner, parents, extended family, or society as a whole? So often, the standards that you hold yourself to have come from these external sources, which become reinforced in your mind through clever marketing, social media, TV and movies, and even the people you surround yourself with.

When you are trapped by beliefs and expectations that are not yours, you can feel isolated and powerless. You may start to question yourself as a parent—"Why am I not able to breastfeed?" or "Why was I not able to have my baby naturally? Isn't that the goal?"—which can trigger feelings of shame.

When these expectations come up, you need to critically explore where they came from and whether they're in line with your values and goals as a parent. Did you really care about birthing naturally? Or is that an expectation that was fed to you through others or the media?

What are parenting expectations you had *before* becoming a parent?

_____

_____

_____

_____

_____

What are parenting expectations you have now?

_____

_____

_____

_____

_____

Are these *your* expectations or someone else's? Are these aligned with your values?

_____

_____

_____

_____

The Comparison Trap

When it comes to motherhood, it's easy to fall into the comparison trap, especially if you're a new mom. Maybe you're pregnant, maybe you just had a baby, or maybe you're chasing after a toddler or two. You're sleep deprived and your hormones are all over the place, which makes it easier for those shame-inducing thoughts to pop into your head: *Wow, how does this influencer with six kids do it all? How do all these other moms have it together when I can barely keep it together?*

The comparison trap is one that you can so often fall into when you are mindlessly scrolling through social media. We haven't met anyone who hasn't fallen into this trap at one point or another, especially given the prevalence of Instagram, Facebook, and TikTok. You are constantly bombarded with images of other parents living picture-perfect lives, which can trigger us to internalize negative self-talk ("I can't do as much as she can. She is such a better mom.") or to become judgmental toward other parents ("Who does she think she is, showing off herself like that?"). It's often easier to criticize yourself or others instead of acknowledging that other parents do things differently from you, and this doesn't mean that you're wrong or not good enough.

Let's say you're scrolling through Instagram, and you come across an impeccably styled picture that your friend, Karen, posted of her morning routine. Your thought dialogue may go something along the lines of "Wow, there is Karen making green smoothies for breakfast again and doing crafts with her kids. Meanwhile, my kids had cheese crackers for breakfast. I will never be a good mom like Karen." The reality is that Karen *is* at it again, but did you know that Karen lost her shit five times while trying to get her kids to pose with their green smoothies? That Karen only functions well in the morning and that the rest of the day is an absolute write-off for her? Social media is a highlight reel, so you don't get to see the other side of Karen—only the side she chooses to portray.

The reality is that social media has made motherhood a completely different experience than it was in the past. Think of how vastly your experience as a parent varies from your mom's—just one generation before. Your parents didn't have this little screen telling them that their friends' children were doing crafts on a Saturday morning or eating a gluten-free, organic, non-GMO diet. While there are some positives that have come from social media (like increased knowledge, education, and support for maternal mental health), it also comes with several downsides.

It is so important to examine your relationship with social media, as it can be either connecting or isolating. Ask yourself what your goal is when it comes to being on social media. Give yourself permission to unfollow any acquaintances or influencers whose perfectly curated photos shift your mood for the worse. If that feels over the top, ask yourself what would happen if you saw a shift in your child's mood or behavior after they were scrolling on social media. Would you permit them to continue, or set some healthier limits around social media?

What is your purpose for being on social media (e.g., learning parenting tips, educating yourself about motherhood, connecting with friends and family, etc.)?

_____

_____

_____

What social media accounts bring out the comparison trap in you? Are there specific images or dialogues on these accounts that provoke negative self-comparisons?

_____

_____

_____

_____

_____

How do you deal with the comparison trap? Do you tend to internalize negative self-talk or push back with judgments?

_____

_____

_____

_____

_____

Early Childhood Experiences

Your early childhood experiences shape the core beliefs that you have about yourself, others, and the world. These are beliefs that you hold true in your mind, whether they're positive or negative. Here are some examples of some common core beliefs:

- I'm loveable (or unlovable).
- I'm safe (or unsafe).
- I'm a good person (or not a good person).
- I am worthy (or worthless).
- I am good enough (or not good enough).
- I will succeed if I try (or I will always fail).

It's important to know that how you were treated as a child (how you were spoken to, lifted up or put down, corrected, disciplined—all these things) dictate the core beliefs that you form. It affects whether you end up believing that you're good enough or not good enough.

Although we could spend the rest of the book talking about the impact of early childhood experiences on core beliefs, we will sum it up by saying that nothing positive comes from being shamed as a young child. When people in authority use shame to control a child's behavior ("Stop being a brat!" "You are a bad girl!" "You should be ashamed of yourself for acting like that."), the child internalizes those messages into their sense of self, and it becomes the inner dialogue they tell themselves.

These earliest experiences of shame tend to stick with you as an adult. Even if you don't explicitly remember what the other person said or did at the time, you can often remember feeling small and wanting to run away and hide. Those feelings just don't go away.

What was your earliest experience of shame? Even if you can't remember the specific details of what happened, what feelings does it bring up as you think about it now?

_____

_____

_____

_____

Many people think becoming a parent can bring a sense of healing to their own childhood wounds. But more often than not, children can cause triggers if you have some sort of shame hiding in a dark corner. Inevitably, your child will behave in a way that sets you off and, out of frustration, you'll revert back to what you were told or shown as kids. You can then slide down a shame spiral, where the messages you tell your children trigger feelings of shame within you. It becomes a vicious cycle that keeps repeating itself.

What shame triggers does your child sometimes bring up for you? The expectations that you hold for yourself, especially when you don't meet them, can be big sources of shame.

_____

_____

_____

_____

MANAGING SHAME IN THE BODY

When something triggers shame within you—whether it's a comment about your body, a parenting stressor, scrolling through social media, or a situation that does not go as planned—you experience a physiological reaction in your body. If you have experienced shame, you likely know it as that feeling of wanting to hide or disappear. It is characterized by a variety of physical sensations such as tightness in the chest, tingling in the hands, and tension in the shoulders. Some people describe it as a sinking feeling in their stomach or shakiness in their body. Anxiety, dread, and even panic can really put these body sensations into high gear. As a result, you may feel the urge to make your body as small as possible, and you may notice that you start to slump, lower your gaze, and pull back from others. It is a feeling that is impossible to forget, no matter how much you want to.

What is a shame-inducing thought that you often struggle with?

_____

_____

_____

_____

_____

_____

What do you notice in your body when you have this thought?

_____

_____

_____

_____

_____

_____

When you are in this kind of shame spiral, the first thing you need to do is bring back a sense of calm to the body. As psychologists who work with trauma from a body-focused perspective, we know that you can't simply "talk" your way out of shame. Instead, you have to start by noticing what you feel in your body when you're ashamed, acknowledging it, and then using tools to help your body regulate itself.

Breathing is the single easiest and most effective skill you can use when you want to calm yourself, as it circulates oxygen through your body and activates the parasympathetic nervous system, which promotes the rest-and-relaxation response. Another one of our favorite grounding strategies involves tapping your knees in an alternating pattern, switching from left to right, to calm your nervous system.

On the following pages, we provide several exercises that focus on the use of breathing and tapping to alleviate shame. Try all of these when you are feeling regulated. You are much more likely to remember to use these interventions in times of distress if you have practiced them when you are calm and regulated.

Exercise
Square Breathing

Although deep breathing is often met with an eye roll and a hefty degree of skepticism ("Oh sure, all I have to do is change the way I breathe and everything will be okay?"), we cannot underestimate the power that the breath has to regulate your nervous system. When you take deep breaths, it truly does allow you to relax your body, settle your mind, and keep your cool in times of stress. The key is to make sure that you are practicing deep breathing correctly, as taking rapid, shallow breaths can actually increase anxiety.

To take a proper deep breath, simply inhale deeply and slowly through your nose until you feel your diaphragm expand and fill with air. You'll want to inhale through your nose, as opposed to your mouth, as this helps slow the breath and makes your lungs work more effectively. It also helps transport the oxygen throughout your body. Once you feel your stomach fill with air, pause for a moment, and then slowly breathe out of your mouth, emptying all the air from your lungs. You should notice your belly deflating as you push all the air out.

In order to incorporate deep breathing into your routine, we encourage you to try square breathing, which is quick and easy to learn. This can be especially helpful when big emotions start to rise and you have difficulty slowing your brain down.

The steps for square breathing are as follows:

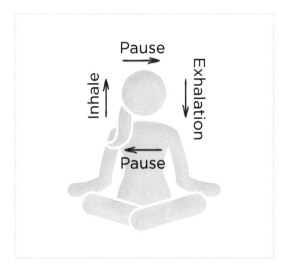

1. Breathe in through your nose for a count of 4.

2. Hold for a count of 4.

3. Breathe out through your mouth for a count of 4.

4. Hold for a count of 4.

Repeat this cycle a total of 4 times or until you feel a sense of calm.

Exercise
Soup Breathing

While there are many different types of deep breathing exercises, soup breathing is another one of our favorites because it simplifies the process so much. All you need to do is simply imagine that you have a delicious bowl of soup in front of you with steam rising from it. Let this be a bowl of soup that you have enjoyed in the past or that you have been looking forward to enjoying in the future.

Then take a deep breath in through your nose—inhaling the aroma of the soup and breathing in all its goodness—and exhale out of your mouth—blowing on the soup to cool it off. Again, inhale the delicious aroma of the soup, then exhale so you can see waves rippling through the soup as your breath meets the surface. Repeat this until you feel a deep sense of relaxation in your body.

Exercise
Bilateral Tapping

Your nervous system is composed of two different branches that work in concert with each other: the sympathetic nervous system (which controls your fight-flight-freeze response) and the parasympathetic nervous system (which helps you rest and relax). When you're stuck in a shame spiral, your brain reacts as if it were confronted with a real threat, which causes your sympathetic nervous system to turn online. This can send you into a state of fight, flight, or freeze that is hard to get unstuck from.

In order to quiet your sympathetic nervous system in these moments, you can combine the use of mental imagery and bilateral tapping, which stimulates each hemisphere of the brain through a series of alternating right and left movements. This works to engage the parasympathetic nervous system, which helps you feel more relaxed and at ease.

To begin this exercise, visualize a place that you find peaceful and calming. This can be a location that you have visited before or simply one that you envision in your mind (perhaps the calm place you described in chapter 1). As you bring to mind this peaceful place, begin slowly tapping on your knees in an alternating right-left pattern. Do this as long as you would like, for a minimum of eight taps on each side.

Whenever feelings of shame get activated in your body, simply try this exercise and notice the feelings of relaxation that emerge in your body.

MANAGING SHAME THOUGHTS

Once you have practiced tuning into your body and using body-based techniques to manage feelings of shame, the next step is to challenge shame-inducing thoughts and to replace them with more helpful coping thoughts. To do so, it's important to become aware of what your shame thoughts are saying in the first place. Here is where it's useful to use the STOP technique:

Stop, pause, and don't react. Visualize a big red stop sign in front of you, and tell yourself (using your own name), "Stop, _____, stop."

Take a couple of deep, full breaths.

Observe what you're thinking and feeling. Notice the thought you're having and label it as a shame thought: "There's that mom shame thought again." Then do a quick body scan, notice where you're holding tension, and breathe into the tension.

Put it in perspective by asking yourself what others would say. What is the evidence this thought is true or not true? What would a neutral observer say? Then come up with an alternative coping thought you can tell yourself instead.

The STOP technique can ground you back into your body and prevent you from falling into an anxious or negative thought spiral. It is very effective when used frequently. In order to get you into the habit of using the STOP technique, look at the following examples of shame thoughts versus coping thoughts, and then fill in the rest of the chart with examples from your own life. While it may be difficult to reframe shame thoughts into coping thoughts at first, the more you practice, the easier it becomes.

SHAME THOUGHT	COPING THOUGHT
I am a horrible mother.	I am the best mom for my child.
I'm such a monster, I don't even know who I am anymore.	I am a good, loving person who makes mistakes sometimes.
I am a disappointment.	I am okay just the way I am.
I do not deserve happiness.	I deserve happiness.
I am worthless.	I am worthy.

You can't get rid of shame—remember, it's a universal emotion—but you can become aware of thought patterns that send you into a shame storm. Unlearning the thoughts that are no longer of service to you is hard work, so remember to have some self-compassion for yourself during this process.

SHAME RESILIENCE

According to Brené Brown (2006), a world-renowned author, speaker, and shame researcher, *shame resilience* is the ability to recognize when shame occurs and having the vulnerability and courage to move through the experience by sharing it with others. Shame resilience is about reaching out to others for connection and empathy instead of moving into isolation and disconnection. According to Brown, the four elements of shame resilience are:

1. Recognizing your triggers for shame

2. Understanding the external expectations that can lead to shame

3. Connecting with others who provide support and empathy

4. Sharing your shame stories with those who deserve it

So often, the fear of your shame being exposed is enough to prevent you from speaking your truth. It is like a cone of silence that keeps you in the darkness. But while no one likes to talk about shame, the reality is that the less we speak of it, the more power it has.

If you want to silence shame and take away its power, you must reach out for connection by sharing your story with others who deserve it—this means those people who make you feel heard, seen, and valued. And it's important to know that you do not have to share *every* detail of the shame. Share what you feel is necessary, or what you would like to get off your chest. To help you cultivate the courage to share your own shame story, Caitlin is going to share her own experience with shame, one that made her want to crawl in a hole and never come out. She hasn't shared this experience on social media before because it felt too intimate on such a public platform, but she felt a level of comfort sharing it here:

I was expecting my first child in the summer of 2016 when I had a very traumatic experience within a very close relationship. The kind of experience that knocks the wind right out of you and makes you question your worthiness. My closest relationship was ending—with someone I thought was going to be with me my entire life—and I felt hurt, blindsided, and alone. As a result, thoughts of "I am not enough," "I have nothing to offer," and "What is wrong with me?" permeated my everyday existence. On top of this, I had just found out I was pregnant, which made the trauma even more complex and filled with heartache.

My initial reaction was to hurt the person who had hurt me. I wanted them to feel the suffering and pain that I did. I was so angry. Was this anger valid? Absolutely. Was I tempted to share my story with people who really didn't deserve to hear it because I wanted to make the person who hurt me look bad in their eyes? Absolutely. I wanted to post it to Facebook—to the whole world!—so the person who hurt me would feel a deep sense of shame and unworthiness, just like I did.

However, I didn't do any of those things. Instead, I shared my shame story with people who loved me, cared for me, and had my best interests at heart. I shared the pain that was eating away at me. The power of connection killed my desire to go out and get revenge. I doused my burning emotions with connection and empathy, which quashed most of the shame I was feeling.

Not everyone deserves to hear your shame stories. Although it might feel tempting, not every person on your Facebook friend list is the right person to witness your vulnerability and pain. So who does deserve to hear your story? Those who sit with you. Those who don't try to make it better, who simply say, "This is so hard." Those who give you a call and stop by when you quit responding to texts.

Who deserves to hear your shame story? Who makes you feel heard, seen, and valued?

_____

_____

_____

_____

What part of your shame story do you want to share with them?

_____

_____

_____

_____

All you need is one person with whom you can be vulnerable, one person with whom you can take off your mask and share your story, and then a domino effect occurs. You realize that you're not alone and you're not the only one struggling with mom guilt. This has been our own experience in sharing our struggles with postpartum anxiety and depression with our Instagram community. Was it easy? Heck no! It was uncomfortable. However, it released a *lot* of other moms to share their stories with us. Their stories of secretly suffering with so much anxiety that they could barely leave the house. Their stories of having intrusive thoughts that their family would be better off without them. Their stories of getting stuck in beliefs like "I am the worst mother in the world. I am not meant for this." When these thoughts are met with secrecy and silence, it can have an excruciatingly painful effect. But when they are met with acceptance and connection, it inoculates us from the effects of shame.

TAKEAWAYS

Although there is no such thing as the perfect parent, so many of us get wrapped up in the desire to be the "ideal" mom that we get triggered into shame mode. Whether this mom guilt stems from our early childhood experiences, our expectations of ourselves, or the comparison trap, when we tell ourselves that we're failing at motherhood, it can really take us for a wild ride into the depths of shame. Shame in the body, shame in the mind, and shame that permeates so many aspects of our everyday life. We can even become so accustomed to the experience of shame that we don't know anything different. Although it takes a lot of work and reflection to break through the outdated and conflicting messages we receive as mothers, it is possible. By having the vulnerability to speak with others and share our experiences, we can come to realize that we are not alone, and we are not the problem.

10   Mother Wound

The *mother wound* can be thought of as the pain and trauma that is carried by mothers and passed down across generations. This trauma is a result of living in a patriarchal society where women are taught that they are less-than or not good enough. We receive these messages from every possible source—from school, from the workplace, from the church, and even from larger society,—and internalize them as our own. We keep recycling this internalized oppression, from generation to generation, across centuries and centuries.

This wound is often felt on the inside and rarely noticed on the outside, yet it has the ability to impact generations of women. We've heard from countless mothers who have ended up being the peacemaker for their parent's dysfunctional marriage, who have always felt a sense of competition with their mothers, or who have struggled with a lifetime of depression, dysfunctional eating patterns, or feelings of inadequacy. In this chapter, we will discuss what the mother wound looks like, signs that you may have experienced the mother wound, and finally, ways to go about healing the mother wound.

THE MOTHER WOUND TODAY

Bethany Webster (2021, p. xvi), an expert on female empowerment, has described the mother wound as a "form of cultural and familial trauma specific to those living in a patriarchy." This can look like a young daughter saddled with the task of caretaker for her mother, who is also burdened by her own relational trauma. It could look like a mother who is constantly told to stop complaining and be grateful she has children. It could even be the young mother constantly mistreated by her spouse and extended family, but who keeps on justifying their behavior to herself.

Although times are changing, and we are now living in a trauma-informed society where patriarchal behaviors that have been tolerated for centuries are being exposed, the mother wound is still something we all continue to experience. That's because society continues to fail mothers by reinforcing harmful stereotypes that encourage women to conform to what others want, to not rock the boat, and to make people happy. Some of these stereotypes include beliefs like:

- Mothers should be kind and loving all the time.
- Mothers should be in control of their emotions.
- Mothers should give everything for their children.
- It should feel natural to be a mother.
- Bonding and connecting with your baby should feel instant and instinctual.

How many of you heard these messages from your own mother while growing up? "You must be kind all the time," "You always need to put on a smile," or "Don't let others know you are struggling." Some of these messages were likely passed down from your mothers' mothers, and while they might be well-intentioned, as mothers simply want the absolute best for their children, the reality is that these messages continue to perpetuate an atmosphere of oppression among women. Therefore, even if you have an amazing mother, the wound can still be there for you. It is inherent in the society that we live in, and in the generations of mothers whose voices and needs went unheard.

What stereotypes have you seen mothers subjected to?

_____

_____

_____

_____

_____

What stereotypes have you personally experienced?

_____

_____

_____

_____

_____

WHAT THE MOTHER WOUND LOOKS LIKE

Jeanine left home when she was 17, feeling both enormous relief and enormous guilt as she went. She was the youngest of three siblings, and the older two had already left years ago, rarely coming back to visit. But she knew why. She didn't blame them. It was easier to stay away than to deal with the chaos in the household.

Growing up, she and her sisters often found themselves protecting and defending their mother, who struggled with addiction, depression, and anxiety. Although Jeanine wanted so badly for her mom to deal with her own demons, she also felt the pull of responsibility whenever her mother seemed to spiral. Jeanine rarely talked about her family around others and felt a sense of embarrassment whenever the topic came up. Having recently bought her first home with her partner, Jeanine would love to have kids, but she feels unequipped to handle parenthood. The question of whether she could pass her family's dysfunction on to her own kids plagues Jeanine often.

Katie grew up in a religious, upper-class family in the Midwest. Her upbringing appeared as perfect as a Christmas card portrait. However, her family placed a large focus on the academic achievements of her brothers, as the goal was for them to take over their dad's medical practice. Katie, meanwhile, was to marry someone well-off, stay home, and have kids—just like her mom did. However, this was not in the cards for Katie; despite no support from her family, she went to college to make a career for herself. She did have a baby last year, but has found it hard to navigate new parenthood while continuing her education. This challenge has prompted unsolicited comments and advice from her family, including eye rolls and frequent "I told you so" comments. While Katie's story of the mother wound is different from Janine's, it still results in the same feelings of rejection and shame.

When individuals suffer from the mother wound, it can lead them to feel ashamed and unworthy. They may constantly compare themselves to others and feel like they can't achieve anything significant. For Jeanine, this wound manifested as doubt that she could be a loving, caring mother. For Katie, it manifested as doubt that she could simultaneously handle a baby and a career. It's worth pointing out that Katie's mother likely suffers from the mother wound as well, seeing as she gave up much of herself to help her husband and family thrive. Therefore, when

Katie was presented with an opportunity to have both a career *and* a family, this angered her mother, leading her to reject Katie.

Often, the pain and struggle of the mother wound can emerge in a variety of dysfunctional coping behaviors, such as having poor boundaries, allowing others to mistreat and walk all over you, or emotionally caretaking others. It can also manifest in competitive urges to outdo other women, the feeling of needing to hold back your authentic self, or a lack of connection with or acceptance from your mother. These are all signs that the mother wound may be affecting you.

PEOPLE PLEASING AND THE MOTHER WOUND

It is important to note that the mother wound does not always need to involve toxic mothers, dysfunctional families, or overt neglect. It can also manifest in less obvious ways, such as chronic people pleasing. We are both recovering people pleasers ourselves. This is one trait that we often see in females, and specifically mothers: the urge to make people happy, to keep everyone satisfied, to not rock the boat. While both men and women can certainly be people pleasers, this trait was likely adaptive for the survival of the female species, as in the history of our patriarchal culture, women who did not act in the service of pleasing others likely did not survive.

This people-pleasing behavior becomes ingrained as early as childhood. As young children, we are often quick to pick up on what makes people happy, what makes people laugh, and what people like about us: "Oh, she is such a fast runner! Oh, she is such a quick reader! Oh, she is such a good helper!" We learn that people value these qualities, so what do we do? We do more of what makes other people happy, and eventually, this can be to the detriment of our own needs and wants. If this sounds familiar to you, let's take some time to explore people pleasing in your family.

What qualities did you need to exhibit to feel accepted in your family? Was it being sweet and quiet? Was it being the smart one? Was it always putting others first?

_____

_____

_____

_____

_____

What qualities were pushed away or discouraged in your family? Was it setting boundaries? Was it having different interests or hobbies that your family deemed unacceptable?

_____

_____

_____

_____

_____

HEALING THE MOTHER WOUND

Now that you realize how impactful the mother wound is, what can you do about it? We've been asked this question by so many moms who recognize their mother wound but are unsure how to go about healing it. The first step in this process is to critically explore your upbringing and the messages you've received from those around you so you can create beliefs that are your own, not someone else's.

Contrary to popular belief, healing the mother wound does not just involve blaming our mothers. It involves becoming aware of the unhealthy patterns, values, and beliefs we've been holding and making a conscious effort not to pass these on to the next generation. Therefore, we want you to take some time to explore the beliefs you were told and to determine what you want to take and what you want to leave. There may be some beliefs you want to hold onto ("It is important to be kind and help others"), while others you want to leave behind ("You must always put others before yourself" or "A good mother always sacrifices herself for the needs of her family").

What beliefs were you told growing up?

_____

_____

_____

_____

_____

Which of these beliefs did you internalize? For example, "You need to make people happy" or "Strong girls don't cry."

_____

_____

_____

_____

_____

What is a new belief you can tell yourself?

_____

_____

_____

_____

In addition, healing the mother wound involves acknowledging what you have lost or given up in the face of motherhood. When you become a mother, your whole world changes, and suddenly there may be things that you never get to do or dreams that will never be fulfilled. Therefore, a significant part of not passing on the mother wound involves acknowledging all that you have sacrificed to become a mother, and giving yourself the space to grieve. For example, there is a small part of Caitlin that always wanted to live in New York City. When she visited the city in 2013 before having kids, she decided that she wanted to figure out a way to live and work there. However, this dream never came to fruition because of her schooling, career, and kids. Given where she currently is in life, it's unlikely to happen, but by acknowledging this loss and creating a space within herself to be sad, she won't allow it to fester inside.

For many of us, the losses that accompany motherhood can lead us to find ourselves at an intersection between gratitude and grief. You are so grateful for your baby, yet you also grieve your old life. This is a topic that we have seen come up time and time again in our online community. The reality is that you are allowed to love your children and also miss what could have been. You are allowed to grieve, and you are allowed to be grateful. When you make space for both of these emotions, you move toward acceptance of your new role and begin to heal the mother wound.

What did you sacrifice to become a mother? What are some things you gave up or have less of in your life (e.g., time, spontaneity)?

_____

_____

_____

_____

_____

What are some of the reasons you are grieving this loss? For example, maybe whatever you lost was something you were passionate about or it was part of your self-care.

_____

_____

_____

_____

What are some things you have gained (e.g., perseverance, strength)?

_____

_____

_____

_____

How can you be grateful about having gained these things? For example, maybe you learned to better attune to your values and to discard all the extra "fluff" taking up space in your life.

_____

_____

_____

_____

Finally, if you struggled so much with your own mother, you might be wondering if you will ever find healing. Often, women who have difficult relationships with their mother hold out hope (sometimes consciously and sometimes unconsciously) that maybe one day, things will be better. That maybe one day, their mother will be the mom they needed her to be. However, when we hold out this hope, we run the risk of being disappointed and hurt every time we make ourselves vulnerable and try to connect. Instead, it is important to remember that the mother wound has been passed down through generations of mothers. It is a deep-seated wound that extends beyond your own mother and even her mother. It is a wound stemming from a patriarchal society that continues to perpetuate myths of motherhood and harmful stereotypes. To break the cycle and heal, you must recognize these stereotypes and push back against them so your daughters (and their daughters) do not carry on the mother wound.

TAKEAWAYS

We are all a product of our family of origin, and centuries ago, people didn't talk about the impact motherhood can have on women. For so long, mothers suffered in silence, avoiding shame by keeping mental health struggles to themselves. Recognizing the mother wound does not mean that you *have* to feel anger or frustration toward your mother, although it's perfectly understandable if you feel that way. Instead, it is an opportunity for learning, growth, and maybe even some much-needed conversations about how to break unhealthy patterns. This doesn't happen overnight. If you are interested in a deeper dive into the mother wound, we highly recommend that you explore Bethany Webster's book, *Discovering the Inner Mother: A Guide to Healing the Mother Wound and Claiming Your Personal Power.* We're proud of you for being here.

11 Where Did I Go? Finding Yourself After Baby

Prior to having a baby, you likely had a great deal of freedom. You were able to go wherever you wanted, whenever you wanted, and you were able to get out of the house in under five minutes. Maybe you went on a lot of vacations. Maybe you enjoyed simple days lying in bed watching television or going to the coffee shop at the spur of the moment.

But life shifts when baby comes, and so many things change. All of a sudden, you have this tiny being to take care of, who also happens to suck up so much of your time. From the naps that revolve around a certain schedule, to the endless baby gear that needs to be sterilized, to the quest to make mom friends while figuring out how to connect with your partner when you're exhausted. Your identity can get lost in the mix of all this. It's easy to focus on simply surviving through the days, only to look back months later and think, *Where did I go?*

In this chapter, we will explore the push and pull of motherhood, the myths of motherhood (and let's be honest, these myths plague both new and seasoned moms), and the value shift that occurs when you become a mom. We'll also give you some tools to help you rediscover yourself.

THE MATERNAL IDENTITY SHIFT

When Caitlin was younger—somewhere between ages 8 and 10—she had this idea that she would have eight kids: four boys and four girls. And she would have them all before she turned 20, so she'd essentially be a young mom with two sets of quadruplets. Sounds fantastic, doesn't it? As she approached her teenage years, she knew she still wanted to become a mom, but she wasn't thinking about having kids in the near future. Fast-forward to her twenties, when her friends from high school started having babies, and she knew motherhood still wasn't for her. She was focused on where she was going with her education and career, and having kids was still a someday-in-the-future thought. Well, that "someday" finally came, Caitlin found out that nothing can really prepare you for the identity shift that happens when you go from being an independent person to someone's everything.

Before you became a parent, you probably had a good idea of who you were, what you enjoyed, what you were good at, and what you found important. Basically, you had a sense of individuality, and that's what set you apart from others. But once that baby came, you were no longer just an individual—it was suddenly you plus baby. The night before you went into labor was the last time you were truly ever "alone."

This transition into motherhood, known as *matrescence*, was coined by medical anthropologist Dana Raphael in 1975, but it still isn't as widely talked about as some of the other identity shifts that occur during our lives. Just think about the identity shift that occurs during adolescence, which is a wild ride, to say the least. It's a well-known fact that adolescence is a time of identity exploration and tumultuous emotions. We expect that there will be tough times for teenagers undergoing this shift. Given the sheer amount of emotional and physical changes that kids go through during this stage, no one is shocked by how difficult this transition is. Why isn't there this same recognition for mothers? Pregnant women going through matrescence experience enormous changes to their body, emotions, and hormones as well, but many people are still completely unaware of the sheer amount of change during this transition.

THE PUSH AND PULL OF MOTHERHOOD

Even after having kids and talking about maternal mental health every day, we hadn't even heard of matrescence until Dr. Alexandra Sacks discussed it in her popular TED Talk in 2018. In her talk, she discussed how the push and pull of motherhood can lead us to feel like something is wrong with us. After having a baby, you may feel depressed, overwhelmed, or anxious, and on top of this, you come to believe that we're wrong for feeling this way. That you should be feeling something else—something more *magical*. After all, shouldn't you be so grateful for all of this? This push and pull can feel unnatural and perhaps even unsettling, mainly because it is not talked about.

When it comes to the "pull" of motherhood, Sacks describes how the release of oxytocin following childbirth helps you focus your attention on the baby, which allows you to develop a strong attachment with your child. However, while this is happening, your mind is undergoing a simultaneous "push" as you remember your previous life, relationships, hobbies, needs, and desires that will no longer be the same. (Let's be real: How many of you wish you could shower alone or use the bathroom without an audience?) Together, this tug-of-war emerges between the pull of the baby and the push of your old identity, and you are not quite sure *what* to feel.

THE MYTHS OF MOTHERHOOD

Part of the reason that women experience this internal push and pull during matrescence is because they have come to believe a variety of myths about motherhood. These myths make the transition of becoming a parent more challenging and make mothers feel like they're failing at motherhood with this new identity. We asked our community the myths they were told about motherhood, and here some of the common responses we heard:

1. **Bonding is natural and will happen instantly.** Going into labor and delivery, you have this expectation that your baby will come out, they will be placed on your chest, and you'll instantly feel love. While this sometimes happens, it is definitely not always the case. Some moms don't feel an immediate connection with their baby and only develop this bond over time.

2. **Breastfeeding is best.** Although this message has been passed down from generation to generation, the reality is that as long as your baby is healthy and fed, *that* is what's best. Many women also don't realize how difficult breastfeeding can be. It is a huge learning curve for both Mom and baby. Issues with latching, engorgement, anxiety, stress, and more can play a role in the breastfeeding journey of moms.

3. **A good mom can push through anything.** For so many of us, the kitchen could literally be on fire and we would say, "Oh no, I'm fine! I have this under control. I'm fine. I don't need any help." However, learning to ask for help is such a crucial part of parenting. You simply can't do it all. This was a tough learning curve for both of us, as we hated the idea of inconveniencing anyone. But once we pushed

through this uncomfortable feeling, we realized how much better it felt to receive help.

4. **You need to love every second of motherhood.** Cue the collective laughter! No, you don't. And no, you won't. It does not make you a bad mom for not loving every second. Being a parent is rewarding, but it's also demanding, exhausting, and tiring.

5. **You will find your mom squad.** Sometimes you will, but sometimes you won't. Sometimes a village of people shows up to support you, and sometimes they don't. It takes time and some trial and error to find the right people for your mom squad. They may not necessarily be in the first mom group you join, so we urge you to keep looking if you find that a certain group doesn't really work for you. In addition, you might not be besties with everyone in the group, or even a quarter of them, and that's okay. For example, out of the six mothers who were in Caitlin's Mommy and Me class, she stays in touch with one.

6. **Holding your newborn will spoil them.** It is impossible to spoil a baby. Research has even proven this time and time again. Newborns have basic needs to be comforted, soothed, fed, and changed, with some infants requiring more soothing and comfort than others. That is literally how they begin developing a sense of secure attachment with the world. Each baby is so different, so if anyone tells you that you're spoiling your baby by holding it, you can calmly tell that person that the research states otherwise.

7. **Your breasts will go back to the way they were after you finish breastfeeding.** Let's all take a moment to laugh together at this one.

A women's breast size increases up to threefold during lactation, so it's not realistic to expect that they'll return to the same shape and size afterward. While the exact experience will certainly be different for each person, it's likely that your breasts will feel and hang differently after breastfeeding. However, that doesn't mean they are any less beautiful! It's important to remember that you nourished a human being (or several) with these fine ladies.

8. **Older generations know better just because they've raised kids and survived.** Speaking from our clinical experience, we have seen *tons* of people who "survived" their childhood, but we want our kids to do more than just survive. We want them to thrive. While there is no such thing as a perfect parent, with each generation, we find better, more helpful, and more effective ways to do things. We aren't still sitting around using Windows 95 on our computers, are we? Of course not—we've found faster and more efficient ways of doing things. The same can be said about parenting. Our frameworks change, our beliefs shift, and we debunk old theories that are found to be untrue. In fact, generations of adults have made it a point to *not* pass on the unwanted features of their own childhood.

This is just a snapshot of some of the myths that our community shared with us. We dive in to shatter myths like these in more detail throughout this book's individual chapters. For instance, breastfeeding—and all that comes with it—is tackled in chapter 4. We know you've got questions. We've got your back.

What are some of the myths that you were told regarding motherhood?

_____

_____

_____

_____

_____

How have these myths affected your view of parenting (or even your view of yourself)?

_____

_____

_____

_____

_____

At the end of the day, it's so important to remember that the myths of motherhood are just that: myths. They have been passed down to us from our parents, our friends, society, and the media. However, when these myths become "shoulds"—that is, when we internalize them as truths that we need to be living up to—they get in the way of being able to discover our own paths as mothers.

REDISCOVERING YOURSELF

As we've discussed, having a baby can change nearly every aspect of your life. We know countless career-minded mothers who have lost their identities once their babies arrived. We've also heard from so many mothers who are simply wondering who they are in life besides a mom. Does that sound like you? Have you found yourself wondering, *Who the hell am I now? What do I even enjoy doing?* If so, take some time to explore the following questions to help you rediscover yourself.

What are you curious about?

_____

_____

_____

_____

_____

What are some hobbies or activities that interest you?

_____

_____

_____

_____

_____

What are you passionate about? What gets you fired up?

_____

_____

_____

_____

_____

In order to integrate these parts of your pre-baby life into your current life, pick one hobby or activity that you listed—whether it's writing, drawing, or doing your makeup—and make a plan to spend 15 minutes of your day pursuing this interest. Where can you find these 15 minutes? Typically, we find it most effective to sneak in these 15 minutes at the beginning of the day before anyone else is up, or during the day when the baby is napping.

Where can you get your 15 minutes in? What hobby or activity will you do during this time?

_____

_____

_____

_____

_____

For activities that you can't just sneak into your day—such as traveling, going out on date nights, or having some kid-free alone time to work out—it can be a little trickier to find ways to incorporate these into your routine, but it doesn't mean you should put them on pause indefinitely. Instead, decide how often you'd like to pursue this activity so that you're filling your bucket, and come up with a plan to make this happen. For example, perhaps you decide to go on date nights once a month, so you enlist the help of family, friends, or babysitters in your area. Or maybe you want to travel once a year as a family, so you begin the process of vacation planning at the start of every year. Or perhaps you decide to restart a weekly fitness routine, but going to the gym has become an obstacle, so you find some at-home workout classes that fit your schedule instead. Whatever it is, make it a point to integrate it into your life.

What is a more time-consuming or involved activity that you want to make time for?

_____

_____

_____

_____

_____

How often would you like to engage in this activity (daily, weekly, monthly, yearly)? What is a plan you can implement to bring this to fruition?

_____

_____

_____

_____

_____

THE VALUE SHIFT

Values are, in the simplest sense, what is important to you. For example, one person may value alone time, while another person may value socializing with others. One person may value spending time in nature, while another person may value reading and learning. There is no one correct set of values. It will differ for each and every person.

What you find important in life often changes when you become a parent. For example, working was a priority for us before we were mothers, and if we were called in for an extra shift, we'd drop everything to take it. But after we became parents, 9 times out of 10 we wouldn't volunteer for that extra shift unless we needed a break from the kids. Our priority became spending time with our family. The extra money just was not a priority anymore.

Although it's a given that your values will shift to some extent with motherhood, some of these changes will be more noticeable, while others won't be quite as apparent. Take some time to reflect on how your values have changed as a result of motherhood. When you can pinpoint your values, you can better prioritize what is important to you and leave out all the rest. This can help you behave in ways that are consistent with who you want to be in the world. It can also help you set clearer boundaries and develop and maintain relationships. Remember, your values are there to support *you*.

How did your values shift when becoming a parent? What became more important?

_____

_____

_____

_____

_____

What became less important?

_____

_____

_____

_____

_____

TAKEAWAYS

When you're expecting, you spend so much time preparing for the birth of your baby that you often forget that you are preparing yourself for the transition to motherhood as well. Although there are many identity shifts that occur throughout your life, the change that comes with being a mother is arguably the biggest of all. It is a change that causes tension, as the pull of the baby competes with the push of your old identity. However, life does not stop after you have a child. You can make time to explore your passions—those things that get your blood flowing—while still being a mom. You can embrace your new identity while not losing sight of the other things that make you, *you*.

12 NICU/Preemie Moms

This chapter is near and dear to Chelsea's heart. Not only is she a former NICU and preemie mom, but she was also born premature at 36 weeks. She was told by many to not worry about it when it came to her own pregnancy: "Premature births are so rare. How would that also happen to you?" As her pregnancy went on, she blocked this possibility from her mind and didn't expect that it could happen to her. But it did, and in a big way. Here is her story:

My son was born at 27 weeks, 5 days gestation—otherwise known as 12 weeks premature or 3 months early. He was even born in the wrong year. (This one stuck with me a lot.) My day seemed to begin like many others, but reflecting back, I can remember the moment my contractions started. I was sitting in a local coffee shop when I had a cramp. I chalked it up to having drank too much tea. I carried on with my workday, not feeling well but assuming I was just experiencing typical aches and pains of pregnancy, seeing as the third trimester was looming just a few days away.

Fast-forward to the end of the day, where I was having four cramps an hour. I decided to call my local hospital and ask what I should do. They assured me that if my cramps felt manageable, they were likely Braxton-Hicks contractions; still, they said, I should come in if they got painful. So off to bed I went. As a new mom, I was scared to go to the hospital, scared to be considered that irrational new mom who was taking up the health professional's time. Well, midnight came, and it was painful. My husband bribed me to go to the hospital (through the possibility of returning home with chicken nuggets) and off we went. Turns out I was in full-blown labor and 5 cm dilated. As scary as it was, I was very lucky to have a wonderful support system.

Enter the NICU part of my story. The city we live in does not have a Level III NICU, a subset neonatal unit for infants born at less than 32 weeks old or under 3.3 pounds, so after my son was born, the neonatal transport team had to take him to the correct hospital, which was two-and-a-half hours away from our home. We were separated for the first 32 or so hours as I stayed in our local hospital overnight. I would be lying if I said this was hard at the time, mostly because I was in shock and didn't realize what was happening. But looking back now, I feel robbed of the opportunity to hold my baby.

Once my husband and I arrived at the new hospital, our NICU stay was a roller-coaster, to say the least. We lived in the Ronald McDonald House, a charity organization that provides support for families with children undergoing medical treatment. I truly can't say enough good things about this organization. Through donations and amazing volunteers, families have access to homemade meals, snacks, treats, and a room to stay in (for as long as needed) at a very low cost. It became our home away from home for three months. There we had a place to sleep that was five minutes from the hospital, but more importantly, we got to connect with other parents struggling through their children's medical journey. These people became our family. We would share our good days and bad days with them, or we'd just sit around and talk with them when we needed a distraction. Although there were a lot of ups and downs, and it felt like a lot to handle, it was comforting to know that our journey wasn't that abnormal.

Our journey in the NICU lasted about 15 weeks total. We celebrated Halloween, Christmas, New Year's, and our son's due date all in the hospital. In my head, I was determined to be out before Valentine's Day (and we were—by two days). After we were discharged, I think everything that I had been avoiding finally crept up on me, and I experienced some postpartum depression symptoms. It's hard to say if these symptoms would have been there anyway, but I do know that I struggled once we returned home. No more monitors. No more NICU nurses. No more empathetic parents. Just tons of doctors' appointments, tons of questions, and tons of fear. We were dealing with normal new parent stuff, NICU stuff, and preemie stuff to create a giant, jumbled mess.

Although our time in the NICU felt never-ending, it now feels a bit like a distant memory (after therapy and support). I am grateful for how this experience shaped and changed my life in a lot of ways. However, it made a time that was supposed to be full of love and excitement filled with heartache. I carried a lot of guilt regarding the NICU with me, and every now and then, the guilt still rears its ugly head. I don't think I will ever completely leave my experience behind, but I do want you to know there is healing that can happen during and after your NICU/preemie journey.

In this chapter, we are going to break down some strategies and concepts that often arise when it comes to spending time in the NICU or having a premature baby. While these two experiences aren't always synonymous, they often go hand in hand. So before we jump into some strategies, let's break down some definitions and statistics.

DEFINITIONS

NICU

The neonatal intensive care unit (NICU) is the unit that will care for babies who are born with complications or concerns until they are able to go home. Hospitals have a few different types of neonatal care, depending on the type of care your child needs. The names may vary from hospital to hospital, but here are some general descriptors:

- Level I (Well Newborn Nursery): Basic newborn care
- Level II (Special Care Nursery): Babies born at 32 weeks+ who need some specialized care and support before going home
- Level III (NICU): Babies born at less than 32 weeks gestation
- Level IV (Regional NICU): The highest level of care, often for babies who need surgical support or who have congenital conditions that need specialized treatment

Gestational Age

Gestational age, which is measured in weeks, is used to define how far along a pregnancy is. It is measured as the number of weeks that have elapsed since a woman's last menstrual cycle.

Premature Birth

A premature birth occurs when a baby is born more than three weeks before their intended due date, which is predicted by their gestational age. According to the World Health Organization (2018), 15 million babies are born premature every year. Prematurity causes challenges in a variety of areas. The following are subcategories of prematurity that are impacted by gestational age and birth weight:

- Micro-preemie: Less than 25 weeks
- Very preterm: Less than 32 weeks
- Moderate preterm: 32 to 34 weeks
- Late preterm: 34 to 37 weeks

- Early term: 37 weeks to 38 weeks 6 days
- Full term: 39 weeks through 40 weeks 6 days
- Late term: 41 weeks through 41 weeks 6 days
- Post term: 42 weeks and beyond

STATISTICS

According to the March of Dimes (2011), 49.1 percent of NICU stays are due to preterm birth, while 50.4 percent of stays are for term babies who require intensive support. The remaining 0.5 percent consists of babies who are delivered post-term. The average NICU stay is just about two weeks.

In the United States, the preterm birth rate is roughly 10 percent, while in Canada, it is approximately 8 percent. In our province of Alberta, we sit at about 9 percent (March of Dimes, 2021; Canadian Institute for Health Information, 2021).

MANAGING GUILT AND SHAME

There can be some intense feelings of shame and guilt after experiencing a NICU stay or having a premature baby. You might be thinking, *I feel like it's all my fault. What did I do wrong?* We often hear from parents who feel like they missed something or did something wrong, as if the experience was somehow in their control. This is often the furthest thing from the truth. There are a variety of unavoidable reasons that your baby may have been born prematurely or had to stay in the NICU.

REASONS FOR NICU STAYS	REASONS FOR PREMATURE BIRTH
• Respiratory concerns • Premature birth • Complications during birth • Heart defects • Feeding challenges • Jaundice • Intrauterine growth restriction • Low blood sugar (hypoglycemia) • Difficulty regulating body temperature (or keeping warm) • Other medical concerns	• Problems with the placenta • Pregnancy with twins or multiples • Problems with uterus or cervix • Maternal drug or alcohol use • Family history of preterm births • Having a previous premature baby • Preterm rupture of membranes (PROM) • Physical injury or trauma • Medical conditions (impacting both the mother and child), like diabetes or high blood pressure

There is no single known cause for your baby being born premature or spending time in the NICU. Chances are, there is nothing you could have done differently or better. However, this can be hard to keep in mind while you are plagued by intrusive thoughts that you are to blame. So what can you do? One of the most helpful things you can do is talk to your medical providers about the experience, including anything that didn't make sense to you. Often, you'll come to realize that there was so much out of your control during the NICU experience that it could not possibly be all your fault. For example, you did not have the ability to control the length of your stay, your child's health outcomes, or which medical procedures were necessary during the experience.

Nonetheless, navigating the NICU is hard, so it is important to find ways to help cope with the intense stress associated with the experience. In the following exercises, you'll find some affirmations specifically for navigating the NICU and a thought-reframing exercise to help you work through the roller-coaster of emotions you may be experiencing. As always, if you are struggling, we encourage you to connect with a trained mental health professional to help you process the experience. You can also reach out to your birth support team, including your midwife or doula, to see if they can be a resource for you.

Exercise
Affirmations for Navigating the NICU/Premature Birth

As you may have noticed, we are big fans of affirmations, which are a beautiful way to acknowledge and validate your current emotional experience. Here are some of our favorite affirmations to help you find comfort through any grief, shame, or guilt you are feeling as a result of your NICU or preemie experience.

May I be kind to myself.

I am allowed to grieve and feel disappointment.

This does not make me ungrateful.

There is no right way to grieve.

There is no right way to feel.

May I find the strength and support I need.

It is not my fault.

My body did not fail me.

Exercise
Challenging Negative Thoughts Toward Yourself

Parents often blame themselves when their child is born prematurely or has to spend time in the NICU. In reality, the NICU is often a sudden and unexpected journey that isn't anyone's fault. When you berate yourself with negative self-talk for something that was out of your control, it can add a layer of difficulty to an already overwhelming experience. If you find that this is something you are struggling with, give this exercise a try.

Step 1: Identify the thought. Recognize a thought you have had about yourself regarding the NICU and write it down here.

Example: *I am a terrible parent for letting my child end up in the NICU.*

_____

_____

_____

Step 2: Describe how this negative thought makes you feel. What are the different emotions you feel when you think or say this to yourself?

Example: *This thought makes me feel guilty and ashamed—like I'm the worst mom in the world.*

_____

_____

_____

231

Step 3: Look at the evidence. What is the evidence to support this thought? What are you telling yourself that you did (or did not do) to cause this? Is anyone making you feel bad about your child's hospital stay? Are you creating this narrative toward yourself?

Example: *I keep telling myself that I should have taken it easier during this pregnancy, but I tried to do everything right by eating healthy and staying active, which shows that I'm a good mom. In addition, all the doctors have told me that they couldn't have predicted my son would be born this early. This supports the fact that I'm not at fault, even though I blame myself.*

_____

_____

_____

_____

_____

Step 4: Evaluate the thought. Is this a helpful or an unhelpful thought? Will this thought help or hinder you?

Example: *This thought is unhelpful because I don't have an answer for why this is happening. It is out of my control.*

_____

_____

_____

_____

Step 5: Think of alternative perspectives. If you were talking to your best friend, what would you say if they were having this thought?

Example: *The NICU is not something that anybody would ever choose for their child or their family. This isn't the result of something you did.*

_____

_____

_____

_____

_____

Step 6: Describe how this new perspective makes you feel. What emotions come up when you think of this new thought?

Example: *I still don't like that this is out of my control, but this new perspective reminds me that none of this is my fault. This gives me some degree of solace.*

_____

_____

_____

_____

_____

SURVIVAL TIPS FOR NAVIGATING THE NICU

Trying to learn, understand, and navigate the NICU environment is truly all about survival. There is no guidebook when your child is admitted and no advanced planning that is provided in typical childbirth classes. In fact, a NICU experience are typically not talked about until you are in the thick of it yourself. This can limit your ability to effectively cope with the situation or find ways to support your family. Here are some tips that our clients have found helpful, as well as some strategies that Chelsea and her family learned throughout their experience.

- **Talk to a social worker or psychologist**. If a social worker or psychologist are available at the hospital, they can provide an outlet for you to express your story or voice your concerns in a safe environment. They may also be able to help provide you with some coping strategies that you can use while in the NICU. If a social worker or psychologist is not available, you can also schedule an appointment with your mental health care provider when you're ready.

- **Try not to Google things.** While the internet can be a great resource, we find that the stories presented online often involve extreme black-or-white scenarios. This can provoke anxiety, sending you down a dark rabbit hole. If you have concerns, we encourage you to write down your questions (as it can be challenging to remember them) and discuss these with a health care provider who is familiar with your case or working directly with your child.

- **Look out for the three G's.** Know that three G's—grief, guilt, and gratitude—may pop up regularly. Life in the NICU can be a constant back and forth between feeling high and low. This teeter-totter of emotions can be draining for parents. In order to move through the grieving process, it is important to remember that no emotion is wrong. Allow yourself the space to feel *all* the emotions as they arise.

- **Reach out to other NICU parents or support groups.** Connecting with parents who have gone through similar experiences and understand the roller-coaster of emotions you may be feeling can provide you with a much-needed sense of comfort and community. Chelsea and her husband made lifelong friends through their NICU experience with whom they still communicate to this day.

- **Ask questions.** Whenever you need clarification, ask for a meeting with your health care providers. It can sometimes be confusing to navigate your child's medical concerns or understand the rationale behind any changes being made regarding their care. By sitting down with your child's primary health care providers or the NICU team, you can get a better handle on what is going on.

- **Try to connect with a primary nurse.** Primary nurses are nurses who typically work with your child when they are on shift. If your hospital offers primary nurses, they will likely work with you for the majority of your NICU stay to ensure continuity of care. While Chelsea's son's stay was long, he was able to have a couple of primary nurses, which was extremely helpful since they really understood her son's needs.

- **Attend rounds when possible.** Rounds occur when the NICU team meets to discuss and debrief regarding your child's care and next steps. When Chelsea's son was in the NICU, rounds were completed every morning. She found it helpful to be a part of this experience, as she was able to hear what medical decisions were being made and was able to provide her input when needed.

- **Take deep breaths.** This sounds silly and overly simple, but when your nervous system is stressed and working overtime, it is important to do the simple things. Breathing exercises can help calm your body down and allow you a moment to quite literally catch your breath.

- **Be patient with yourself and your partner.** Although we know this is easier said than done, it is important to recognize that navigating the NICU can put a strain on even the strongest relationships. You and your partner may cope with the stress of this experience in different ways and may find different ways to bond and interact with your child. When you find yourself getting on edge with your partner, remember that just as you are going through this experience, so are they. Try to extend some grace to them (and to yourself).

- **Try not to feel bad for needing and taking breaks.** (And don't feel bad for calling in to check on the baby when taking those breaks.) It is important to have some time away from the hospital, as challenging as it is to do so. Breaks allow you and your partner to rest (hopefully) and to get some much-needed tasks accomplished that you didn't have time to do before your NICU stay. You can utilize this time in whatever way feels best for you. If you feel overwhelmed when you're away, remember that it is also okay to call in and check on your little one, too.

- **Know that the NICU tends to feel like an emotional roller-coaster.** Things can change very quickly in the NICU, leading you to feel the most extreme highs and the most extreme lows. If this resonates with your experience, know that you are not alone and that you are not doing anything wrong. Just take it day by day. Hour by hour. Minute by minute.

WAYS TO BOND IN THE NICU

Bonding as a family in the NICU can feel really challenging, and it may seem like there's not much that you can control or work toward. For Chelsea, bonding as a family took a bit of time and compromise. For example, her son was in the NICU over Halloween, Christmas, and New Year's. She was dead set against celebrating anything—it didn't feel as though they had anything to celebrate—but her husband really wanted to decorate their son's pod area (his "condo," as they called it) for Christmas. With some gentle convincing and unhappy shopping, they decorated his space, and it ended up being an incredibly rewarding experience. Their son had one of the most decorated pod areas for Christmas; even the nurses brought him a few decorations to hang up. While it may not seem like much, it became a way to connect as a family.

If you're thinking of ways to bond in the NICU, know that it's not something you have to do right away, and it might not happen overnight. Rather, it's about finding little things that are meaningful to you and make these hard moments feel special. Here are some things we suggest:

- **Engage in kangaroo care.** Kangaroo care, also known as skin-to-skin contact, is a great way to connect with your baby, and it has a host of documented benefits for both you and your child. Not only does it facilitate bonding, but skin-to-skin contact also releases hormones that can stabilize your baby's temperature, breathing, heart rate, blood sugar, and more.

- **Video chat with family and friends.** When you're not allowed to have visitors in the NICU, it can add a sense of disconnection to what is already a very isolating experience. If you are able to, we encourage you to video chat with loved ones so you can share real-life moments as they unfold. Similarly, share photos of your journey with friends and family as you feel comfortable. Not only does this give you an opportunity to share pictures of your lovely baby, but it also allows loved ones to connect with and understand parts of your experience.

- **Stay nearby.** When you can't hold your baby in your arms, stay as close as the staff will allow you to be. There will be times when, for various medical reasons, you will be unable to hold your child. For Chelsea, the one that stands out the most occurred during the "critical window," which is the period of time right after birth. For Chelsea's family, this lasted for three days. Although she was unable to hold her son during this time, standing nearby still provided a sense of connection.

- **Take time away.** While it seems counterproductive to the last point, you will also need time as a couple away from the NICU, whether you go on an evening date or spend some time at home. The NICU life can become all-consuming, and connecting as a couple for at least a short time can provide you with a sense of normalcy.

- **Play music, sing songs, or read books.** Not only is this a great way to connect with your baby, but it also allows you to do something that feels like a "regular" parent activity, which can provide you with a sense of routine or comfort. In addition, tell your child stories of your family, home, or anything that feels important to you. Storytelling is a great way to pass the time and connect as a family.

- **Make your baby's space your own.** Bring parts of your home to the NICU, such as blankets, clothes, books, or pictures. You can also decorate the space (if allowed). By making the NICU space your own, you'll feel a little more at home in what is a very sterile environment.

- **Pump breastmilk.** Pumping can be a bit of a double-edged sword. Sometimes it can be a triggering experience that feels like a chore, but it's also a great way to make you feel like you are contributing or doing something tangible for your child.

- **Document your journey.** Keep track of you and your baby's time in the NICU through pictures, videos, or journaling. Chelsea was lucky enough that the NICU provided her with a daily journal where she documented her son's medical information, as well as pictures and milestones. Documenting this information allows you to reflect on how far your baby has come (especially when the constant ups and downs make this hard to remember) and provide you with a concrete reminder of your child's journey.

- **Celebrate holidays (even though they may feel bittersweet).** If your child's hospital stay extends over important dates or holidays, you may want to find a way to celebrate those together. As described earlier, for Chelsea's family, that was decorating for Christmas.

- **Stay involved.** Help with diapers, baths, feedings, or other day-to-day care activities as you are able. When you're involved in these types of daily care activities, it creates a sense of connection and helps you feel empowered as a parent. It can also help you feel some semblance of normalcy in what is a very stressful experience.

CARING FOR OTHER CHILDREN AT HOME

Spending time in the hospital when you have other children at home can add a layer of difficulties to the NICU or preemie experience. Parents often express feeling guilt for not giving each child the attention they need or deserve. It can feel like you're being split in two as you try to provide love, care, and support to each child. This balancing act is not easy to juggle, but here are some tips to consider:

- **Focus on quality over quantity.** What do we mean by that? When you are with your other children, provide them with as much undivided attention in those moments as possible. Focus on 15-minute increments if you can. No phones, no television, no multitasking. Just you and your child.

- **Highlight points of connection.** You might tell your child, "You are going to be with _____ while Mommy is at the hospital with the baby tonight. I will see you tomorrow morning when you get up." This lets your child know when you will be seeing them again. Your estimate doesn't have to be exact, but if you know that you won't see them for a day or two, make sure to tell them that. If you're stuck at the hospital, you can do this through a video chat or over the phone. The point is to not leave them feeling uncertain in what can already feel like an uncertain time.

- **Lean on your support system.** Are there people in your life who can help out with your children at home? Friends, neighbors, family members? With whom do you feel comfortable leaving your child? If you don't have a support system nearby and it's just you and your partner, are you able to take turns being at the NICU and being at home? What options feel realistic and reasonable for you and your family?

- **Find ways to include your other child.** This can be done in a variety of ways. For example, are they able to visit? Can they do something special for their sibling, like drawing a picture or sending a note? Are you able to video chat with them from the hospital? Can they buy the baby a small gift? This can help them feel connected to what is going on and allow them to bond with their sibling.

- **Explain exactly what is going on.** If you have younger children, use age-appropriate language to explain why their sibling isn't home (e.g., "Your brother or sister came out of Mommy's tummy a little early and needs some extra time at the doctor so they can grow big and strong."). Validate and acknowledge anything they might be feeling in return. We also encourage you to show your other child pictures of the baby. Not only does this foster connection to their sibling, but it also lets them know that some difficult things are going on.

- **Use affirmations.** Practice mama mantras to acknowledge that you are doing the best you can:

> *This isn't easy, and I am doing the best that I can.*
>
> *May I be kind to myself in this moment.*
>
> *There is no right way to go through this process.*
>
> *I cannot meet everyone's needs at once, and that is okay.*
>
> *I am only human.*

PREPARING TO RETURN HOME

When you are in the thick of the NICU experience, it can be hard to imagine that the experience will ever end. But life after the NICU will come eventually. As you get into those later stages, it is important to start considering what will help you prepare for your return home. Prior to discharge, we encourage you to write down any questions you may have for your current medical team so they can help you with this transition. Here are some additional questions that may be helpful to reflect on before returning home:

- **Who will your medical team be?** Ask your medical provider what types of specialists your child will require after discharge beyond a family doctor or a pediatrician.

- **What community supports do you have access to?** Speak with a social worker or another mental health provider at the hospital who may have insight into funding opportunities or resources that your child has access to because of their NICU stay.

- **What can others do to support you at home if they offer?** Brainstorm what types of tasks people can do that might relieve some of your burden. This can include childcare, a meal train, or even just phone calls or texts to check on how you're doing.

- **What are your boundaries around visitors in your home?** Do you feel comfortable having people come over once your family is settled? Stating these expectations ahead of time can make it less overwhelming once you return home because people will already know what's helpful (and what's not) ahead of time.

- **Do you need any specific medical supplies at home?** Chelsea's son came home requiring both oxygen and a feeding tube, so she needed to have the necessary tanks and tubing. She was also using a breast pump, so she made sure to have the right pumping parts on hand.

- **Are there any additional supplies that would make you feel comfortable?** For example, Chelsea chose not to have a baby monitor to try to get out of the habit of constant observation, but some people feel like monitors are important, especially after a NICU experience.

- **Is there anything you can do while the baby is still in the NICU that would help prepare you?** For example, can you make a few freezer meals at home or schedule some appointments for yourself?

HOW TO SUPPORT SOMEONE IN THE NICU

When someone you know is going through the NICU or preemie experience, it can sometimes feel like there's nothing you can do or say that's even remotely helpful. You might be worried that you'll say the wrong thing and feel at a loss for words because you don't how the NICU parents will respond. We are here to tell you that it is okay to try to gently bring things up. NICU parents often feel misunderstood yet have difficulty expressing themselves and their needs. When you take the first step in initiating a conversation, it opens up the possibility to provide them with some much-needed support and relief. If you know a NICU parent and aren't sure where to start (or are a NICU parent yourself and have family and friends asking what they can do to help), send them the following list!

- **Don't be afraid to ask about or bring up the NICU.** It may seem awkward at first, but most parents appreciate it when loved ones ask them questions or check in on them. And if they are in a place where they aren't wanting or willing to share, they'll typically make that known.

- **Listen without comparison.** It can be hard not to share your own story (or stories that you've heard from other people), but this isn't necessarily helpful (and may even be harmful) when NICU parents aren't looking for unsolicited advice. Instead, provide a compassionate ear without making any comparisons to others' struggles. And if there is information you would like to share, ask them first! For example: "I heard from a friend whose child also spent time in the NICU. Would you like me to share with you some of that experience?"

- **Be forgiving.** They may not be the friend they were before. Remember that your friend is going through an unimaginable experience. They aren't purposefully ignoring you or forgetting important things. Give them some grace during this difficult time.

- **Just do without asking.** Sometimes NICU parents are unsure of what they need in the moment, so it can be helpful to just do things without asking. This can include starting a meal train, sending gift cards, helping with transportation, offering to take care of their other children, picking up mail, doing chores around their house, or just keeping an eye on their place if they are spending long chunks of time away at the hospital. At the same time, be sure to only offer what feels comfortable and appropriate for your own boundaries. You are allowed to have your limits on what you are comfortable and willing to do. That is more than okay.

- **Feed them!** Whether you take them out to eat, cook food for them, or drop off premade meals, one of the most helpful things you can do for NICU parents is make food one less thing they have to worry about.

- **Celebrate milestones with them.** Even small milestones can feel big for a NICU parent, whether it's getting to change their baby's diaper or feed them for the first time. Even though you may not understand why the little things matter, try to celebrate and honor their excitement.

- **Continue checking in.** As the weeks go on—it can be a long haul. NICU parents are often flooded with support in the beginning, but as the time goes on, people move forward with their own lives. Sometimes babies are in the hospital for months at a time or have long medical journeys once they arrive home. If you are thinking about them and want to check in, do so! And don't forget about the non-birthing partner. They're often forgotten in these situations, so if you have a relationship with them, check in with them too.

- **Don't force positivity on them**. It is okay for NICU parents to not feel positive all the time. Sometimes they simply need their struggles or hard days validated. For example, let's say a parent tells you, "We had a really bad day in the NICU. Sometimes I feel like this is never going to end." In this case, a helpful response might sound like "I can appreciate why you feel that way. You all have been through so much. You are allowed to have hard days."

PREPARING FOR SUBSEQUENT PREGNANCIES

If your baby was born prematurely or had to spend time in the NICU, it can be really challenging to decide whether or not to have another child. You may be experiencing a lot of guilt, fear of the unknown, or doubt about whether you could go through it again. Unfortunately, there are no right answers here, and ultimately you must make the best decision for you and your family. Here are some things we recommend when making this decision:

- **Speak with your health care provider about preconception planning.** Preconception planning involves looking at your health and risk factors for preterm birth before you become pregnant. This gives you an opportunity to explore what it might look like to have another child and what your medical options are to increase the chances of a healthy pregnancy. For example, they might recommend certain lifestyle changes, supplements, treatments, or monitoring to help prolong your pregnancy or detect signs of preterm labor.

- **Work with a trained perinatal therapist or a therapist who has experience treating trauma.** Having a baby in the NICU is a trauma in its own right. Before moving forward with another child, we encourage you to work through this traumatic experience so you can heal and make preparations for subsequent pregnancies.

- **Get support.** Speak with your support system, online communities, or with other NICU or preemie parents. It may help to hear others' experiences or outcomes from other pregnancies.

- **Avoid Googling.** Instead, look up reputable sources or join an online support group. Check out some of our favorite resources at the end of this chapter.

TAKEAWAYS

Nothing can truly prepare you for being a NICU or preemie mom. It is an extremely challenging experience, regardless of how your journey goes. We hope that you found some support and comfort in hearing Chelsea's story and learning some tips and tricks for navigating the experience. For more information, be sure to read our chapter on birth trauma as well. Hang in there, Mama, from one NICU parent to another.

OUR FAVORITE RESOURCES

- *Pregnancy Brain* by Parijat Deshpande: Written by a high-risk pregnancy expert, this book focuses on mind-body approaches for stress management during high-risk pregnancies.

- Dear NICU Mama (@dearnicumama): This Instagram page provides resources to support parents who are going through or have gone through NICU experiences.

- Verywell Family (www.verywellfamily.com): This website provides a wealth of information on all things related to pregnancy and parenting.

- March of Dimes (www.marchofdimes.org): This nonprofit organization is dedicated to improving the health of babies. Their website provides information about the perinatal period, as well as for complications that can arise, such as pregnancy loss and NICU stays.

13 Other Types of Mamas & Families

Over the years, the nuclear family—a mom, dad, and a child or children living in the same household—has often been viewed as the "traditional" family structure. However, as society has evolved, our perception of what constitutes a family has really shifted as we recognize many diverse types of families today. This can include families with same-sex parents, blended families, childfree families, and more. Furthermore, people have become more comfortable sharing their family structure and lifestyle habits through social media, which has promoted greater awareness of families that fall outside of what is considered traditional. While there is still stigma surrounding diverse types of families, we hope that the narrative continues to shift with more acceptance and dialogue.

In this chapter, we'll share the many types of experiences that can arise for families of all walks of life. We realize that not everyone reading this book shares the same family structure, and we also recognize that certain families have unique struggles that can feel challenging and isolating. We wholeheartedly want the strategies and tools we discuss in this book to be applicable to moms, dads, parents, and families of all kinds, so we'll provide some information and resources here to those of you who feel like your family doesn't fall under the category of "traditional." First, though, let's hear some stories from different types of families.

STORIES FROM DIFFERENT FAMILIES

Miguel and Steve's Story

Miguel and Steve, who have been together for about five years, feel as though they are ready to take the next step in their committed partnership by starting a family. As they begin to explore their options in family planning, they look into possible surrogates and adoption agencies. After a few years of saving, they move forward with the surrogacy process and welcome twin girls into the world a year later. They are overjoyed to expand their family and adore being parents, but it hasn't come without its challenges. They face significant financial pressure after going through the costly surrogacy process along with frequent stigma when people ask if their children will miss not having a mother. While Miguel and Steve know they can give their daughters all the love and support they need, it can still be challenging to navigate discriminatory and insensitive comments.

April's Story

April is a single mom with two kids, ages 3 and 5, from her previous marriage. She has tried going through the court system to sort out parental rights, visitation, and child support, but her ex-husband isn't interested in participating or negotiating. He hasn't seen her or the children since he left the family two years ago. April often finds herself on the edge of burnout, as her extended family lives in another state and she has limited community support. She is able to get herself and the kids up and ready for school, but by the end of the day, she is absolutely exhausted. She struggles to find time for herself and is unsure how to even begin meeting her own needs. She would love to start looking for a new partner but doesn't know how to navigate the dating world with two young kids.

Donette and Robert's Story

Donette and Robert met about two years ago, after separating from their previous spouses after more than 10 years of marriage. Donette has two children from her previous marriage, while Robert has three. Their children range in age from 3 to 17 years old. Donette and Robert recently moved in together, only to find that the transition has not been as smooth as they'd hoped. Donette is having trouble connecting with Robert's children since they don't view her as a mother figure or an ally. Likewise, Robert has been struggling to find ways to serve in a disciplinary role to Donette's children. Luckily, Donette's ex-husband is supportive, so there is limited confrontation on that side. However, Robert has been in and out of the court system with his ex-wife to determine how they will split custody. Donette and Robert have begun couples counseling to help them navigate bringing both of their families together.

OUR FAMILY STRUCTURES LOOK DIFFERENT

Families truly come in all shapes and sizes, with not every family subscribing to the "traditional" or nuclear family structure. Moreover, different types of families come with their own unique set of challenges and strengths. In this section, we'll explore how some families identify themselves and what these different family structures may look like. While we have tried to do our best to include an exhaustive list, we recognize this is continually changing and will continue to adapt over time.

LGBTQ+ Families

Parents who are part of the LGBTQ+ community can identify as lesbian, gay, bisexual, transgender, or queer. When it comes to family structure, LGBTQ+ families can include same-sex couples, different-sex couples (in which one parent identifies as bisexual or queer), or a single parent who identifies as LGBTQ+. Unfortunately, these families have historically faced significant discrimination by society. Not only do LGBTQ+ parents face stigma and violence in their everyday lives, but their children are often the targets of bullying and harassment as well.

In addition, the journey to becoming parents can often be difficult for many LGBTQ+ families. While some same-sex couples have had children from previous heterosexual relationships, others must go through different means to create a family. This can typically involve donor insemination, adoption, foster care, or surrogacy. Often, there can be challenging legal considerations and financial barriers to navigate during this process, as same-sex couples in particular have had to fight for equal adoption rights. Transgender parents in particular can face challenges with regard to custody disputes, adoption, and relationship recognition (Stotzer et al., 2014).

Two-Spirited Parents

The term *two-spirited* is used by some indigenous cultures when a person identifies with both masculine and feminine energy. The term can be used to refer to how someone identifies in terms of their gender identity, sexuality, spirituality, or cultural role. Often, individuals who are two-spirited do not identify with a particular gender. Although two-spirited families are part of the LGBTQ+ community, this specific term is used in indigenous cultures only. Two-spirited parents are often the targets of racism and homophobia, and they describe feeling isolated, discriminated against, and underrepresented (Rowlandson, 2010).

Adoptive Parents

Adoptive parents refer to parents who take on the legal rights and responsibilities of a child who is biologically not their own. Adoptions often take place in families where there is no familial connection between the parent and child, but in some cases, grandparents and other extended family members can adopt relatives, or a stepparent may adopt their spouse's children. The adoption process can be closed or open, meaning that the birth parents' information is either kept private (closed) or made available to a certain extent (open). In open adoptions, there may also be some degree of interaction between the birth parents and the adoptive parents.

Adoptive parents face many unique challenges, not only related to the adoption process itself, which is a trying process fraught with barriers and financial hurdles, but also in navigating family life after the fact. Many adopted children have been subject to significant trauma—in fact, the act of being separated from their biological parents is a trauma in and of itself—and this can cause attachment difficulties with the adoptive parents. This can be compounded by the fact that adoptive parents often experience discrimination for not having biological children or for having a multiracial family.

In addition, adoptive parents may be navigating their own grief and loss, particularly if they are choosing to adopt because they have been unable to bear their own biological children. They may also struggle with post-adoption depression—similar to the postpartum depression that a birthing parent can experience—likely due to the major life shift that occurs as they transition into a parental role and learn to connect with their child.

Foster Families

Foster families offer a temporary placement for a child when the child's biological parents can no longer support them and the child is unable to be placed with other family members or relatives (known as kinship care). Some foster placement times are longer than others, with children's length of stay ranging from less than one month to over five years.

While foster families can look similar to other families in terms of their day-to-day lives—for example, they care for a child's needs, get them to school every day, and enroll them in sports or other activities—there are some unique challenges that come with being a foster parent. First and foremost, most foster parents have to go through a licensing or screening process to ensure that their home is suitable to provide care. Then they must navigate supervised visit schedules with the birth family, keep up with increased demand for meetings or appointments, and prepare for periodic home visits. Some agencies also have specific regulations and recommendations for foster homes, such as requiring background checks before a foster child can even have a playdate at another friend's home.

There are also several parenting challenges that foster families may struggle with. Being placed in foster care is also an inherently traumatic experience. In addition, children in foster care often exhibit behavioral and emotional challenges because of their experiences in previous homes, which may have involved abuse or neglect. Finally, foster care involves the unique struggle of having to say goodbye when the child is adopted, is returned to the birth parents, or if there is a disruption in the foster placement. This experience can be challenging for both the parent and child.

Grandparent Families

When grandparents take on the parental role for a grandchild, they can do so for a variety of reasons. For example, the biological parents may not be able to offer a stable home environment as a result of addiction, incarceration, abuse, or neglect. This can also occur in the case of military parents who get deployed overseas or teenage parents who require more support in raising their child. In some cases, the grandparents may become the primary caregivers following the death of the parents.

It can be challenging for some grandparents to be thrust into this role, especially if they are struggling with grief, resentment, or frustration over what is happening with their own child, as well as having to provide care for their grandchildren. They may also face unique age, health, and financial concerns about whether they can provide a future or even an education for their grandchildren. Especially for older adults, health concerns can make it difficult to readjust to the parental role again.

Extended Families

An extended family is a family that consists of relatives beyond the "traditional" nuclear family, all of whom live in the same household. Often this can involve multiple generations of family members, such as aunts, uncles, grandparents, and cousins. This type of family structure typically values the supportive role that various family members can provide each other with when living under one roof (Allen et al., 2011). Although this is certainly an advantage of extended families, it can create boundary issues when family members are unsure of or, at times, overstep their roles and responsibilities. Adult children may also find it difficult to differentiate themselves as authority figures when older relatives live in the home. Finally, there may be grief or other complex emotions at play, depending on what role the child's parents play in the family.

Single-Parent Families

In single-parent families, one parent, usually unmarried, widowed, or divorced, is raising children alone or taking on the primary workload. There can be varying levels of involvement from another parent (sometimes referred to as the co-parent), such as a case of divorce or separation, but the brunt of the parenting usually falls on one person.

Not surprisingly, single parents can experience significant financial stress that comes with being a single-income household. Even if there is some degree of monetary support from the co-parent, it can be difficult to make ends meet at times. Similarly, in the role of the primary caretaker, it can be difficult for single parents to find ways to meet their own personal needs, whether this involves engaging in self-care, finding time for themselves, or even trying to start dating again.

Some single parents must also face a variety of challenges in the legal system as they navigate custody agreements, child support, and visitation schedules. They can also experience a lack of support, especially if certain friends or peer groups dissolved after the end of their partnership with the co-parent. They must contend with broader social stigma as well, given that single parents often describe being viewed as less-than or discriminated against due to their marital status.

Blended Families

A blended family typically develops after a separation or divorce, and it is defined as a family in which one or both partners have children from a previous relationship. While blended families are relatively more common than they used to be, they still face the unique pressures that come with living as a stepfamily. These can come in the form of legal disputes that either parent may be navigating with their ex-partner (e.g., divorce proceedings, custody agreements, child support issues), as well as the challenges of managing multiple personality dynamics in the family. Not only is sibling rivalry common among stepsiblings, but stepparents often describe difficulties related to understanding, creating, and compromising their roles as a parent. What is their role in a disciplinary sense? How are they creating relationships with their partner's kids? How does their co-parenting relationship impact the family dynamics? It can also be tricky figuring out how to present a united front when multiple parental figures are involved. It can feel like a lot to juggle.

Polyamorous Families

A polyamorous (or "poly") family can form when three or more adults are romantically involved and choose to raise a family together. In contrast to infidelity or adultery, polyamory is considered a form of consensual nonmonogamy because all parties involved in the poly relationship are aware of (and consent to) the openness of the intimate relationship. Given that the lifestyle choices of poly families are not consistent with traditional cultural norms, they typically describe feeling judged, misunderstood, and stigmatized.

Because of the complexities of poly relationships, it can sometimes be difficult to know the legalities when it comes to custody of the children in the relationship, as well as what role each parent takes in the child's life. When there is an additional adult (or more) in the relationship, parsing out parenting responsibilities and disciplinary roles can get complicated. Finally, if any changes occur within the hierarchy of the poly relationships, which can happen when one relationship disintegrates, it can be difficult to reshuffle the organization of the family and share this news with family members.

Family of Choice

When people no longer have a relationship with their biological family, they can develop what is known as a family of choice, which involves a supportive network of people in that person's life that fulfills the role of a traditional family. Families of choice are most common among individuals in the LGBTQ+ community who often feel abandoned, neglected, or unsupported by their biological family. When individuals do not have the support of their birth family, it can lead to significant feelings of loss, grief, anger, or resentment. However, families of choice present an amazing alternative where marginalized populations and communities can receive the support they need and deserve.

Single-Child Families

When families decide to have only one child (or sadly, that choice is made for them), they are often known as one-and-done families. Unfortunately, there is a lot of stigma that surrounds having only one child, as there appears to be this societal expectation that families need to have more than one kid. Parents will often get asked when they will be giving their child a sibling or when baby number two is coming. For women who are unable to have any more children, this can be extremely triggering. And for women who have made the choice not to have more children, it can feel extremely frustrating. It's an insensitive question, and women are allowed to keep their reasons to themselves without having to justify it.

Overall, it can feel isolating and judgmental when you have only one child. Furthermore, there are a lot of myths of having one child that can make it more challenging. For example, there is the common misconception that only children will be spoiled, lonely, dependent, aggressive, bossy, or disadvantaged. However, the reality is that just like any type of family, there are both positives and negatives that can come from having only one child. These myths are not necessarily true and are certainly not dependent on being an only child.

Childfree and Childless Families

While the terms *childfree* and *childless* are sometimes used interchangeably to describe families without children, they each carry their own connotations. Childfree families generally refer to families that have made the active choice to not have children, while childless families would like to have children but are unable to do so due to circumstances out of their control (e.g., infertility). Similar to the experiences of single-child families, both childfree and childless families often describe feeling judged and isolated. They find themselves fielding frequent questions about why they don't have children or when they will finally conceive. For parents—especially women—who don't have children by choice, this can perpetuate the harmful expectation that having a child is necessary in order to feel fulfilled in life. And for childless families who yearn for a child, these constant questions and judgments only serve as a reminder of what they feel is missing from their life.

Interracial Families

Interracial families, in which multiple family members of different racial or ethnic backgrounds live in one home (Wilt, 2011), are becoming increasingly common in our society. This increase has occurred following the rise in interracial marriages and international adoptions as our society becomes more racially diverse and accepting of different cultures. As interracial families continue to increase, so do the number of biracial or multiracial children, who identify as two or more races. For example, Chelsea considers herself biracial, as she comes from both Japanese and Caucasian heritage.

Although there is often a lot of pride in interracial homes, these individuals still face significant discrimination and social stigma as a result of racism. Multiracial children in particular face several challenges as a result of their mixed-race heritage, and they may be subjected to frequent derogatory comments, struggle when trying to fit in with their peers, and find themselves fielding inappropriate questions about their racial background. This can lead them to feel marginalized, disrespected, or embarrassed. It can also cause them to question their personal identity, as they may feel they don't "belong" to any one race in particular. Interracial families also have unique challenges when it comes to parenting, as there can be cultural differences in parenting styles that create tension and communication challenges between parents in the home.

Neurodiverse Families

Neurodiversity can be defined as functioning that differs from the neuro-normative. Often, individuals experiencing mental health challenges, developmental, or intellectual delays or disabilities fall under this category. Neurodiversity is most commonly associated with attention-deficit/hyperactivity disorder (ADHD), autism, and learning disabilities, such as dyslexia. The idea behind neurodiversity is to highlight that individuals experiencing these challenges have strengths and weaknesses just like anyone else and that it is important to recognize that their brains are wired differently. This is more of a strength-based view that neurodiversity is a necessary part of the human experience. Parents within our community who have neurodiverse children often describe a grief-loss experience, difficulties relating to other parents, and struggles with burnout, as they often have additional or different caregiver roles (e.g., managing medications, medical appointments, advocating).

FINDING THE SUPPORT YOU NEED

The definition of a family is different to everyone and is ever evolving and changing, but when your family structure falls outside the "norm," it can feel isolating and marginalizing, especially if you don't have a group or community that can relate to your experience.

If you're wondering if the strategies we present in the other chapters will still work for you, the answer is: for the most part, yes. Most of these tools—such as learning to challenge negative thoughts, making space for all emotions, and setting boundaries—are important for any family regardless of structure. However, we do recognize that many families face challenges, like significant discrimination, financial barriers, and social stigma (to name a few), that make it difficult, or even impossible, to implement some of these strategies.

In these cases, it is most important to find the resources for your particular circumstance. Reach out to individuals or communities that you find supportive and understanding, or that have firsthand experience with what you are going through. This can involve connecting with professional services, such as a therapist, who can listen to and validate your story, provide you with different coping strategies, and help you address your concerns in a supportive and nonjudgmental environment.

It can also involve looking into online or in-person support groups that provide resources and information relevant to your specific situation.

There is no one-size-fits-all type of support, so it is okay to try out different therapists or look for community resources that feel comfortable to you. In addition, we cannot emphasize enough the importance of engaging in self-care and finding ways to look after your own needs. If this seems overwhelming, start simple and start small. As lovely as it would be to have hours at a time to yourself, this often isn't realistic for many families. Be mindful of what self-care might look like for you. Maybe it is getting in a shower. Changing your clothes. Taking a five-minute breather. We provide a variety of self-care suggestions in chapter 8.

TAKEAWAYS

There can be unique and isolating challenges for individuals whose family structure looks different from the norm. We wanted to take some time to break down what these families often experience, including the isolation they may feel when attempting to build a sense of community or support. If this is the case for you, we hope this chapter has provided you with some further insight and helpful resources to support your family. Remember, even if your family falls outside of what is considered "typical," you are worthy of support.

OUR FAVORITE RESOURCES

- PFLAG (www.pflag.org)

- National Foster Parent Association (www.nfpaonline.org)

- Adopt US Kids (www.adoptuskids.org)

- Loving More (www.lovingmorenonprofit.org)

- The Not Mom (www.thenotmom.com)

- Embrace Race (www.embracerace.org)

- Generations United (www.gu.org)

- National Stepfamily Resource Center (www.stepfamilies.info)

- Impossible Parenting: Creating a New Culture of Mental Health for *Parents* by Olivia Scobie

- *The Case for the Only Child: Your Essential Guide* by Susan Newman

14 Pregnancy Complications & Loss

When you're trying to conceive, your emotions can make you feel like you're on a roller-coaster. You may oscillate between hope, excitement, disappointment, and fear. There may be doubt that you are making the right choice to expand your family, excitement and nervousness for the pregnancy to come, fear that the journey may not go as planned, and anxiety around things that are out of your control. When roadblocks arise as a result of infertility, medical complications, or pregnancy loss, you may question if you'll ever have a baby or if you'll be able to become, and stay, pregnant. It can be a jarring experience that makes you question your identity as a mother.

In this chapter, we hope that you'll find some relatable stories from individuals who have shared with us their experiences with infertility, complications, and loss. In learning more about these challenges, our wish is for you to realize that you aren't at fault and you aren't alone. We know this chapter may be difficult to read and can be triggering for some. Please take your time going through it, read it at your own pace, and take breaks when you need to. We will be here whenever you are ready.

WHAT IS INFERTILITY?

Alison always felt as though she was meant to be a mom. Ever since she could remember, it was something that she dreamed of. As soon as her husband Damion felt ready, they began to try for a family. Alison had hoped it would only take six months, which is the average that everyone hears about, so when she was still trying to conceive a year later, she began to worry. What was she doing wrong? Why were her friends getting pregnant and not her? What was she supposed to do? After consulting with their doctor, Alison and Damion underwent testing to see if they were experiencing challenges related to infertility. When the results came back, they learned that Damion had low sperm motility and Alison had blocked fallopian tubes. They would need some medical support to conceive a baby, and so began their journey to start infertility treatments.

Have you or someone you know experienced a similar story? If so, you aren't alone. Although many individuals struggling to conceive feel like they're the only ones going through the experience, you might be surprised to know that approximately one in eight couples are affected by infertility when the woman is younger than 30. This increases to one in five when the woman is between the ages of 30 and 39 (CDC, 2022).

Infertility occurs when a couple has difficulties getting pregnant after one year of trying to conceive (or after six months if the woman is over 35 years of age). This experience can be taxing to both individuals' mental health and can place significant strain on their relationship as they confront invasive procedures, failed fertility treatments, and societal or personal pressure to create a family. The need for medication, timed sexual intercourse, and financial outlay can all create tension and frustration in the household. On top of that, there can be significant triggers that come in the form of others' baby announcements, gender reveal parties, or maternity photos.

If you and your partner have been struggling to conceive, how you choose to continue the potential journey into parenthood is completely up to you. Here are some options that other families dealing with infertility have considered:

- **Medication.** There are a variety of medications for people struggling with infertility. These include drugs such as Clomid (which stimulates ovulation) or hormonal injections (which can include progesterone or human chorionic gonadotropin, also known as hCG).

- **Surgical procedures.** There are a variety of exploratory and reproductive surgeries that can be performed to determine if something is causing the infertility or impairing conception. These procedures can also involve making repairs or improvements in the reproductive tract.

- **In vitro fertilization (IVF).** This is a complex medical procedure that can help families become pregnant. Typically, eggs and sperm are collected and fertilized within a lab setting, and once an egg has been fertilized, it is transferred to the uterus for implantation and (hopefully) a successful pregnancy.

- **Intrauterine insemination (IUI).** This is a less invasive medical procedure compared to IVF in which sperm is placed directly into the uterus around the time of ovulation to help with conception.

- **Egg and sperm donation.** This involves utilizing a third party's egg or sperm to help conceive a child.

- **Surrogacy.** This is when a woman outside of the couple is the gestational carrier of the baby. However, choosing surrogacy can be a difficult and expensive option for families.

- **Adoption.** Some families will choose the option of adopting a child to expand their family.
- **Going childfree.** Some families will make the difficult decision to remain childfree if they are unable to pursue any additional treatment options.

All of these choices can have an impact on your mental health. You may experience feelings of grief, emptiness, failure, guilt, shock, fear, loneliness, jealousy, and even relief. You may feel a perceived loss of control over your life and a loss of trust in your body. With all these different emotions swirling around, it can be difficult to decide what treatment options are best for you. This is further complicated if you don't have the financial access needed for certain treatments—the average cost of IVF is $20,000, while surrogacy usually comes with a six-figure price tag. It may also be that you do not have the rights to choose certain options. When these reproductive rights—that is, your ability to decide when and if to have a child—have been taken away, it can bring you to your knees.

If you are currently going through infertility struggles, be gentle with yourself and know that there is no right way to feel. Infertility is both physically and mentally draining, so if you find that you are more reactive, less patient, or more worn out, that is to be expected. If you find that you are triggered by other people's pregnancy experiences or can't attend a baby shower, that doesn't make you a bad person.

In order to acknowledge the current struggles you are facing, validate your emotions, and provide yourself with some self-compassion, we encourage you to read through the following affirmation exercise and give them a try.

Exercise
Affirmations for Infertility

Infertility is a long and hard road. It may cause you to feel every kind of emotion from anger to guilt to sadness. The following affirmations are here to provide you with some comfort as you continue your journey to conceive. As with everything we suggest, take what works for you, leave what doesn't, and adapt any of the statements to fit your own experience better.

This is not how I expected my pregnancy journey to go.

I am allowed to be grateful for and frustrated with the medical procedures.

I am hopeful.

This is a hard journey. I am allowed to grieve.

I have the patience and care to help my body.

This isn't going how I planned—may I be kind to myself.

I am capable and strong.

May I have strength through this journey.

My feelings are valid.

COMPLICATIONS IN PREGNANCY

There are many different medical complications that can arise during pregnancy. Given that we are not medical professionals, we won't jump into them all too deeply, but just know that any type of medical complication can add a significant layer of difficulties to not only the physical well-being of a pregnant person, but also to their mental health.

Hyperemesis Gravidarum

When you become pregnant, you often go into the experience mentally preparing for the possibility that you will experience at least some morning sickness during the first trimester. Nothing some ginger candies and plain bread can't help, right? Unfortunately, the term *morning sickness* is a misnomer since it can last well beyond the morning and even—sorry to say—beyond the first trimester. How many of you couldn't bear the sight of food for a good portion of your pregnancy? When Caitlin was pregnant, the mere thought of chocolate (which used to be one of her favorite foods) was enough to make her heave.

Unfortunately, for some women, the nausea and vomiting that accompanies pregnancy comes on far stronger than what is considered typical. Known as hyperemesis gravidarum (HG), this condition results in persistent and severe nausea and vomiting that can last throughout the entire pregnancy, often requiring hospitalization. As HG is an uncommon experience, women who suffer from it often feel isolated and alone. The challenges associated with HG can also affect future decisions regarding family planning, impact the family's life at home (especially if hospitalizations occur), and make pregnancy feel like it may never end (even though rationally you know it does). If you're experiencing HG, you can find additional support and resources at www.hyperemesis.org.

Preeclampsia

You go in to have one of your regular check-ups at the OB-GYN. You know, the kind that you wait over an hour for, only to have a five-minute appointment with your doctor. You've just hit your third trimester and are starting to anxiously count down the days until your due date. As you daydream about your baby, the nurse checks your weight and starts to take your blood pressure. Suddenly she asks how you are feeling. You can tell by the look on her face that something isn't quite right. She leaves the room, and the doctor comes in a few minutes later to let you know that you have preeclampsia. At this point you might be thinking, *Preeclampsia?! What is that? I feel fine!*

Preeclampsia is a condition that causes significantly high blood pressure in pregnant women. If it goes untreated, it can be life-threatening. Typically, women do not experience symptoms at first, but as it progresses, it can result in vision changes, severe headache, and rib pain (English et al., 2015). Unfortunately, this condition does not go away until the baby is born. This can be a stressful condition for mothers to go through because it requires increased monitoring and can also lead to an earlier than expected delivery.

Gestational Diabetes

When women finally make it into the second trimester of pregnancy, they often start feeling a bit better, have a bit more energy, and can still see their feet. It is during this time, typically around the 26th week of pregnancy, that they need to schedule their gestational diabetes test. You know, the dreaded orange glucose drink that every mother complains about—that one. It involves heading over to a community lab, downing that nasty drink as fast as possible, and hanging out for an hour until your bloodwork can be drawn. If the results of the bloodwork indicate that your blood sugar levels are too high, you need to do a formal glucose test. If you fail that test, it means you are likely experiencing gestational diabetes.

Gestational diabetes is a condition that impacts how your body breaks down sugar, which is otherwise known as glucose intolerance (Buchanan et al., 2007). It often has no warning signs at first and is usually caught through the screening test. If gestational diabetes is left untreated, it can adversely affect fetal growth (Buchanan et al., 2012). Luckily, once it is detected, it can be treated with support from your health care provider.

MISCARRIAGE AND PREGNANCY LOSS

When Cassidy and her partner decided to begin actively trying for a baby, they were both shocked and elated when she became pregnant by the second month. Sadly, she lost the baby in the first trimester. While this was devastating for Cassidy, she knew that she wanted to continue to try. After a couple of months, they began trying to conceive again, only for Cassidy to quickly become pregnant and experience another first trimester loss. Cassidy was starting to lose hope that she would ever have a baby, and she felt anxious and overwhelmed at the idea of becoming pregnant again. She also felt like she couldn't talk about her experience with anyone. She worried about making people feel uncomfortable and was unsure if anyone would even think it "counted" as a loss because it happened so early on in her pregnancy. She didn't know where or to whom to turn, so she kept it to herself and struggled in silence.

As Cassidy's story illustrates, there is often this veil of secrecy around miscarriage, and women are often encouraged to keep news of their pregnancy private until they get past the first trimester. This can make women feel isolated despite the fact that miscarriage is a very common experience, with one in four women enduring a pregnancy loss at some point during their reproductive journeys (Bardos et al., 2015). Moreover, there is truly no "safe" point in pregnancy, and families should have the choice to share and celebrate when they feel comfortable doing so. A miscarriage can be one of the most vulnerable times in a woman's life, so there should be conversations, support, and empathy available for those going through the experience. Bereavement is not something that is meant to be walked through alone. While the stigma is slowly shifting regarding this narrative, we still have a ways to go.

Although many women blame themselves after experiencing pregnancy loss, there is often a medical reason for why a miscarriage occurs. This can include genetic abnormalities, chromosomal abnormalities, and structural difficulties within the placenta, uterus, or cervix (Bardos et al., 2015). However, this knowledge still provides little comfort to those experiencing a miscarriage, as it doesn't take away the grief or pain of the loss or the worry of another miscarriage during subsequent pregnancies.

PREGNANCY LOSS STATISTICS

- 80% of miscarriages occur in the first seven weeks.
- Up to 25% of pregnancies end in miscarriage, which is one in four women!
- Over 80% of miscarriages have no known cause.

HOW THE MEDICAL COMMUNITY DEFINES MISCARRIAGE AND LOSS

Although *miscarriage* is the overarching term that's often used to describe the loss of a pregnancy, there are many other terms that describe this experience. Loss can happen in many different ways and at many different stages. We've heard from so many women who've felt like many of their personal types of loss have been overlooked.

Therefore, we think it's important to break down some of these additional terms, as they can get really complicated, and we know that some of our readers will find comfort in learning about these labels so they can define their loss for themselves. We hope that by highlighting some of these terms, you feel a bit more seen. Please know that when we provide the definitions below, we are using the actual medical terms, so by no means are we trying to use insensitive language.

- **Threatened miscarriage.** A condition in which there are warning signs of a miscarriage, such as vaginal bleeding or cramping. Sometimes the pregnancy can continue, and sometimes it will end in a completed miscarriage.

- **Completed miscarriage.** The state when all pregnancy tissue has been removed from the body. This can happen naturally or with medical support.

- **Chemical pregnancy.** A pregnancy that occurs and is lost before pregnancy can be detected.

- **Molar pregnancy.** A pregnancy that fails to develop properly.

- **Blighted ovum.** A gestational sac that develops without a fertilized egg or fetus inside.

- **Ectopic pregnancy.** An embryo that implants outside of the uterus, often in the fallopian tubes. Surgery is usually required, and the fertilized egg does not often survive.

- **Missed miscarriage.** Also known as a silent miscarriage, this occurs when the fetus no longer continues to develop but you continue to experience symptoms of pregnancy.

- **Incomplete miscarriage.** A condition in which some pregnancy tissue remains in the uterus after a miscarriage. Sometimes a medical procedure is needed to ensure all the tissue has been removed and the woman is safe.

- **Recurrent miscarriage.** When there are repeated miscarriages in a row, usually defined as three or more consecutive miscarriages.

- **Termination for medical reasons.** When a fetus has a severe medical condition that will prevent it from surviving outside of the womb (or that will result in a short and difficult lifespan), families are offered the option to terminate the pregnancy before going to term.

- **Abortion.** Also known as termination, this involves the removal or ending of a pregnancy. An individual may choose to end their pregnancy for any reason, whether they feel unprepared to bring a child into this world or have other health concerns that make pregnancy risky. Some women have described feeling forced into an abortion by their partners or families. There is often a lot of stigma surrounding termination and abortion.
- **Second trimester loss.** Sometimes called a late miscarriage, this is a loss that occurs between 12–22 weeks of pregnancy.
- **Third trimester loss.** Also called late trimester loss or stillbirth, this occurs when there is a death of the fetus after 20 weeks of pregnancy.
- **Neonatal loss.** This refers to a baby who passes away within the first 28 days of life.

It is important to know that everyone is going to label their own pregnancy loss differently. How you define your loss is 100 percent up to you. Yes, there are lots of medical terms that define this loss, and some of you may find comfort in that, but others need an opportunity to explore what the loss means to them before they can put a label on it.

TRYING TO CONCEIVE AFTER PREGNANCY LOSS

Trying to conceive after experiencing a pregnancy loss can be an extremely triggering and emotional process. Many women fear that they will go through a similar experience again. Along with feeling unsure if they have the emotional and physical capacity to handle another loss, they may also wonder how they will feel as the pregnancy progresses. *Will I be judged for trying too soon? For waiting too long? If I get pregnant right away, will it take my pain away?* There are so many questions that can run through your head. These questions, concerns, and emotions are completely understandable and to be expected.

If you are deciding whether to conceive after a loss, just know that there are no "right" answers about what is best for you. Pay attention to your own internal cues that you are ready to try again. This is a completely individualized experience, and there are no right or wrong answers here, but "being ready" might involve feeling hopeful about trying again or noticing a decrease in your grief or anxiety. We also encourage you to have an open and honest conversation with your partner to gauge their readiness to try again. Finally, seek professional support if there are any medical considerations guiding your decision, or if you need help navigating your grief before trying again. If you are currently going through any type of pregnancy loss, or are experiencing pregnancy after a loss, we invite you to read through the following affirmations.

Exercise
Affirmations for Pregnancy Loss

If you have experienced any type of pregnancy loss, we encourage you to read through the following affirmations, especially if you have been unable to (or have struggled to) share your experience with others. As always, take what works for you, leave what doesn't, and adapt any of the statements to fit your own experience better.

I am allowed to grieve.

There is no right way to feel about this experience.

May I forgive myself.

May I be kind to myself.

There is no timeline for my grief.

Affirmations for Pregnancy After Loss

There is often a mixture of emotions that can arise when you are carrying another baby, and the following affirmations can validate your emotional experience as you attempt to embrace both the positive and negative emotions that may come with the experience. With all affirmations, take what works for you, leave what doesn't, and adapt any of the statements to fit your own experience better.

I have overcome many obstacles to be at this place.

I am still learning to trust my body.

My body knows what to do.

I am doing what I can to have a healthy pregnancy.

I will hold onto hope.

Each day is another day closer.

May I find the courage and strength I need.

I can take it one day at a time.

My feelings and fears are valid.

DEFINING GRIEF

The grief that surrounds pregnancy complications, infertility, and loss can be all-consuming. It can be filled with intrusive thoughts, numbness, and yearning for a life you have dreamed of (Kersting & Wagner, 2012). A lot of people say it feels as though they are drowning. Because grief is such a complicated, messy, and deeply personal process, it can be challenging to put a specific definition on it. Ultimately, how you describe your grief experience is what matters.

Given that the experience of grief and loss is not something you typically prepare for, it often takes parents by surprise. For example, Mariah was thrilled when she first learned that she was pregnant. When the time came to attend her eight-week appointment, she and her boyfriend were excited to see their little bean on the screen for the first time. As she laid back on the table and felt the cool gel on her belly, she knew this was going to be a life-changing moment. Unfortunately, the experience *was* life-changing, but not in the way that she had hoped. The ultrasound technician was unable to find a heartbeat, and it was then that Mariah learned she was having a miscarriage. The waves of grief took her by surprise. She hadn't even considered that she could lose this baby and hadn't heard of anyone in her life who had experienced this loss before. How was she supposed to feel? What was she supposed to do? The next few weeks were filled with tears and uncertainty about the future. While she knew that she wanted to try to conceive again one day, she wanted more time to grieve and process what happened.

When navigating grief related to loss or infertility, there are many possible ways that people process the experience. Some individuals may feel like they are unable to process or speak about their grief because they don't feel like others will view their loss as a "real" loss. For others, the grief may affect their family planning goals or create feelings of self-doubt during subsequent pregnancies.

If you have experienced grief and loss while trying to conceive, know that there is no right way to manage the complicated emotions that come from these difficult journeys. Allow yourself the time and space to heal in a way that feels right to you. If you feel comfortable, please answer the following reflection questions at your own pace to help you navigate your grief journey. If it feels triggering or difficult, please feel free to skip over the questions.

What emotions would you use to describe your grief experience related to infertility, complications, or pregnancy loss?

_____

_____

_____

_____

What thoughts come up when you reflect on your grief experience?

_____

_____

_____

_____

Is it hard or easy to put this experience into words?

_____

_____

_____

_____

Are you allowing yourself to acknowledge the grief you are experiencing? Why or why not?

_____

_____

_____

_____

How are you telling yourself to handle this experience?

_____

_____

_____

_____

If you feel like you need additional help on your healing journey, we encourage you to reach out to a therapist who has experience in perinatal grief, loss, and infertility. We also suggest connecting with a support group of individuals going through similar struggles who can share in your experience. And as always, write down any questions that you have for your medical providers instead of looking online at questionable sources.

WAYS TO SUPPORT A GRIEVING MAMA

If someone you know is going through perinatal grief—whether it's related to difficulties trying to conceive, pregnancy complications, or a loss of any kind—there are several things you can do to support them:

- **Focus on doing instead of asking.** Sometimes grieving parents don't know what they need. Instead of asking, take the initiative to do something kind, whether it's dropping off a meal, helping them care for their other children, offering them rides, or sending them a gift card. However, only offer what is within your ability and comfort level. You don't need to go above and beyond that.

- **Ask them about their loss.** Although you might be worried about saying or doing the wrong thing, people often want to share their experience when given the chance. (And if they don't, they will tell you.) Importantly, listen to their story and allow them to speak without judgment or trying to problem solve in any way. People in the midst of grief just want to be heard and supported. Resist the temptation to offer platitudes, make comparisons to other people's journey to conceive, or offer them solutions.

- **Be patient with their grieving process.** Some people take longer than others to go through the grieving process. Allow them the space to do so and continue to check in on them even as time has passed. The grieving process may take time.

TAKEAWAYS

The pregnancy journey is not an easy one and, for many couples, can be marked by grief, loss, uncertainty, hope, fear, and disappointment. We hope this chapter helped provide some insight into your own fertility and reproductive journey. Whether you experienced one loss or many, went through several rounds of IVF, or experienced unexpected medical complications during pregnancy, know that your struggle and story are valid. You get to define what grief or impact means to you. As you read this, we hope you know you are not alone.

OUR FAVORITE RESOURCES

- *I Had a Miscarriage: A Memoir, a Movement* by Jessica Zucker
- *The Miscarriage Map Workbook: An Honest Guide to Navigating Pregnancy Loss, Working through the Pain, and Moving Forward* by Sunita Osborn

The mom who stares at the baby monitor all night.

The mom who worries that she's made the worst decision of her life.

The mom who mentally relives her traumatic birth over and over again.

The mom who feels angry all the time and doesn't understand why.

The mom who is so scared for her baby's health that she repeatedly washes her hands and checks on her baby.

15 Baby Blues & Perinatal Mood Disorders

After many months of being pregnant, lots of worries, endless appointments, tons of preparations, countless sleepless nights, and one heck of a delivery, your baby is finally here! And now what? In comes the rush of hormones, the need to adjust to motherhood, and sometimes the experience of grief, loss, or altered expectations. Whether it is baby number one or baby number six, it can be difficult to transition to life with a child (or another child) in your family. Maybe things didn't go how you'd hoped. Maybe having a toddler running around the house while you're trying to get your newborn to sleep has been more challenging than you thought. Maybe you miss the part of your old life where you were able to get uninterrupted sleep. There are so many factors that make the first few weeks with a newborn difficult.

In this chapter, we'll touch on a variety of different perinatal mood disorders and compare and contrast these with the typical baby blues. We'll also look at signs and symptoms for each condition and provide you with strategies you can use to help you get through it. The entry into motherhood can be overwhelming, but there are ways to navigate it.

BABY BLUES

The baby blues refer to the sadness, mood swings, and crying spells that many women experience for a period of time after giving birth. Depending on the literature you read, up to 80 percent of mothers report having the baby blues after giving birth. This translates to approximately four in five women, meaning the chances are quite high that you will go through this experience. Although the exact reason for this phenomenon is unknown, it is assumed to result from a combination of factors associated with the birthing process, including major hormonal shifts, sleep deprivation, the anxieties and difficulties that come with transitioning to a new role, and the demands of a newborn. Even non-birthing parents can experience the baby blues as they navigate the exhaustion, time away from work, and identity shift that accompany parenthood.

Some of the signs and symptoms associated with the baby blues include:

- Feeling emotional or triggered more easily
- Crying for no apparent reason
- Difficulty sleeping (even when the baby is asleep)
- Feeling restless
- Having mood swings (switching from happy to sad to excited to hopeless)
- Difficulty attaching to or bonding with your baby or partner
- Missing aspects of your old life and identity
- Forgetfulness or difficulties with decision-making

The baby blues will typically start to improve or resolve within a couple of weeks. On average, they last about three weeks postpartum. If your symptoms continue later into the postpartum period and the severity continues to get worse or stays the same, this is often a warning sign that a perinatal mood disorder may be present. We'll explore these disorders in greater detail later in this chapter.

Our number one recommendation for coping with the baby blues is to do some proactive work by developing a postpartum coping plan. (Even if you are newly postpartum, this can still be accomplished!) Use the following exercise to recognize your triggers, warning signs, and the support and resources you have for help with postpartum coping.

Exercise
Postpartum Coping Plan

Fill in the following information to help create your postpartum coping plan. A completed postpartum coping plan is included first, followed by a blank template for you to fill in your own information.

My anticipated due date: _____

My typical warning signs of distress:

> Not eating
> Being easily angered
> Feeling grumpy
> Headaches
> Crying more frequently

My typical coping strategies:

> Taking a bath
> Scrolling through social media
> Sleeping
> Watching my favorite show
> Calling my mom

My support people:

> My mom
> My sister
> My friend Noel

Resources in my community:

My OB-GYN
My doula
My midwife
My family doctor
My yoga studio/gym
Crisis Text Line (text HOME to 741741)
Postpartum Support International (www.postpartum.net)
The National Suicide Prevention Lifeline (1-800-273-8255)

My partner's role in supporting me after baby is born:

Taking one night shift a week
Giving me a 10- to 15-minute break when they get home
Doing check-ins during the day via phone or text
Being in charge of bath time

Boundaries that may be important with family and friends:

Calling before coming over
Washing hands before holding the baby
Not coming over if sick

Postpartum Coping Plan

My anticipated due date: _____

My typical warning signs of distress:

_____

_____

_____

_____

My typical coping strategies:

_____

_____

_____

_____

My support people:

_____

_____

_____

_____

Resources in my community:

_____

_____

_____

_____

_____

My partner's role in supporting me after baby is born:

_____

_____

_____

_____

_____

Boundaries that may be important with family and friends:

_____

_____

_____

_____

_____

Now if you just read through that coping plan and thought to yourself, *I am past that*, and I *don't think a postpartum coping plan will help. What do I do?!*—know that there are still some general coping strategies that can be helpful during this time period. Here are some suggestions.

- **Practice affirmations (or mama mantras).** These can be phrases like, *A hard day does not make me a bad mom, My baby and I are learning and growing together*, or *This is a moment in time—it will pass*.

- **Eat a meal or snack.** Checking in with your basic needs is important. Taking a moment to get a bite in can quickly improve your brain function and energy level.

- **Rest or sleep when possible.** We know that it is easier said than done! However, it is really important to be mindful of getting enough rest, and sometimes this can involve leaving the laundry for another day and putting your feet up for a couple minutes (or taking a nap if time allows). Sleep deprivation makes it harder to function.

- **Get some movement.** Physical activity is so good for your body and mind. Find ways to incorporate gentle and comfortable movement into your routine, whether it's stretching, yoga, or going for a walk.

- **Do something each day that you enjoy.** This doesn't have to involve something major. It can be as simple as watching a show you enjoy, listening to music, or drinking a cup of warm tea—anything that lifts your mood.

- **Lean on your support system or seek professional help.** This can involve connecting with professional services available in your community (such as a doula or lactation consultant) or reaching out to your personal connections. If you are finding that your mood is not improving, accessing a trained therapist (if possible) can be beneficial in exploring what is going on and helping you find coping strategies.

- **Practice deep breathing exercises.** While breathing exercises may seem too good to be true, they are a great way to settle your nervous system down and regulate yourself.

- **Try bonding activities with your baby.** When you're disconnected from your baby, it can make you feel like a "bad parent." While this could not be further from the truth, engaging in activities with your baby can begin to build that connection. Some people find this through feeding activities, while others enjoy bath time. Explore what activities enhance connection for you.

- **Know that you did nothing wrong.** The baby blues are extremely common, and you did nothing to cause it.

Remember, small and simple is okay! Do what you can when you can. There is no right way to cope. Some days it's literally having a chance to change your pajamas or brush your teeth. Other days it's journaling, getting a full night's sleep, and meditating. It doesn't have to be an hour every day. Even if you can focus on a strategy for a couple minutes a day, that is a great start. As always, it is important to talk to a health care provider if you are noticing that any of these symptoms continue past a few weeks or worsen in intensity.

If you are the partner of someone with baby blues, it can feel extremely challenging to know how to best support them. Although there is nothing you can do to stop them from experiencing it, there are some ways you can help:

- **Create and discuss the postpartum coping plan together.** By working on this collaboratively, you will both feel more prepared to recognize any warning signs and respond as a team. Sometimes it can be difficult to recognize your own warning signs—this way you can keep an eye out for each other.

- **Be patient with them.** Know that they are not trying to be difficult or reactive on purpose. Parenthood is a monumental transition for everyone involved, and many emotions can arise during this time period.

- **Allow them to get rest.** Rest is such an important piece of mental health. As you are able to, give them opportunities to catch up on sleep or take a break. This can help them feel less overwhelmed.

- **Help them bond with the baby.** Help with things like bath time, feedings (if they are on a bottle system), cuddling, or reading.

- **Remember to take care of yourself too.** This is also a transition period for you! By making sure your needs are being met, you can have more energy in your tank to support your partner.

POSTPARTUM DEPRESSION

Postpartum depression (PPD) is arguably the most well-known of the perinatal mood disorders, so let's dive right in. PPD is often known as a clinical depression that arises during pregnancy or in the first year after giving birth. About 10 to 15 percent of postpartum women will experience this type of depression, making it the most common of the perinatal mood disorders. While there is no singular cause of PPD, risk factors include a history of depression, higher-risk pregnancies, low social support, and increased stress (Ghaedrahmati et al., 2017). Your personal feelings about the pregnancy and your relationship dynamics can increase this risk, particularly if you and your spouse are struggling in some other way.

Some of the typical signs and symptoms of PPD include:

- Difficulty sleeping or resting when able to
- Changes in appetite
- Low self-confidence
- Reduced interest in activities you used to enjoy
- Loss of interest in life
- Negative thinking
- Crying spells
- Hopelessness
- Difficulties communicating needs and/or experience
- Withdrawal from others
- Feeling emotionally shut down or overwhelmed
- Muscle tension
- Overwhelming fatigue
- Suicidal thoughts
- Difficulty bonding with your baby

Although there is the common misconception that only birthing mothers can get PPD, dads, partners, and adoptive parents can get it too.

You read that right! It isn't just birthing moms who can experience these struggles. So what does it look like for dads? For men, the symptoms of PPD can look different, as they are typically accompanied by greater irritability and impulsivity. Men with PPD may suddenly withdraw from the family and begin working long hours or drinking excessively in an attempt to cope with their symptoms. They may suddenly lose interest in sex or other activities that they used to enjoy. As fathers adjust to their new role as a parent and try to meet the needs of the

Signs of Postpartum Depression in Dads

Difficulty attaching with the baby

Isolation or withdrawal

Isolation from peers or family

Increase in work

Concerns about productivity and providing for the family

Loss of interest in previously enjoyed activities

Fatigue

Difficulties with sleep

Frustration, anger, or irritability

Crying or emotion dysregulation

Suicidal thoughts

Difficulty with identity change

family, they often feel more helpless or as though they can do less for the baby. This can cause a lot of internal pressure and stress, leading to an increased risk for PPD.

For adoptive parents, depression during the perinatal period is often called post-adoption syndrome, and it involves many of the same symptoms as PPD. However, these symptoms can be further complicated by feelings of isolation, the stigma surrounding adoption as the "second-best" route to parenthood, lack of resources, and difficulties obtaining social support, especially for adoptive parents in the LGBTQ+ community.

Postpartum Depression vs. Baby Blues

It is often difficult to distinguish between the baby blues, postpartum depression, and typical adjustment to parenthood. However, there are two things we typically look at:

1. **The duration of the symptoms.** The baby blues typically last for a shorter period of time, often just a few weeks, after which symptoms begin improving.

2. **The severity of the symptoms.** While the baby blues can feel distressing, the symptoms of PPD are more severe and interfere with your ability to cope with day-to-day tasks.

When considering the difference between the baby blues and PPD, Chelsea has found it hard to define her postpartum experience, given that it was complicated with a premature birth and NICU stay. However, when she was discharged from the hospital, many of her experiences skewed toward PPD (and likely also reflected some adjustment difficulties and trauma from the NICU experience). For example, she found that her mood was low, she had difficulty feeling joy in activities that used to bring her enjoyment, and she experienced an increase in anger. Her personality was also a little more muted, and she withdrew from others and had difficulty sharing what she was experiencing.

If you believe that you're struggling with PPD, we recommend seeking out the support of a mental health provider or other medical professional who is trained in perinatal mood disorders. They can provide you with tools to better navigate what you are experiencing and, if necessary, prescribe medication to treat your symptoms. We also recommend looking at online or community support groups for PPD, who can help you better understand your experience.

In addition, don't underestimate the importance of taking care of yourself at home. Check in on your basic needs throughout the day. Have you had something to drink or eat? Do you have a moment to shower or change your clothes? Once you're cleared to exercise, try moving your body, whether you simply go for a walk or stretch at home. Exercise can provide you with some much-needed endorphins that lift your mood. Finally, make sure to rest and get some sleep when you can. We know this one is frustrating to hear and can feel impossible with young children at home, but if there are moments where you can put your feet up or get some consecutive hours of sleep, this can be extremely beneficial in easing some of your symptoms.

POSTPARTUM ANXIETY

Although PPD tends to get most of the press when it comes to perinatal mood disorders, over the past several years, postpartum anxiety (PPA) has become increasingly recognized within the mental health community. Affecting around 17 to 20 percent of new moms, PPA refers to excessive periods of worry, dread, and racing thoughts during pregnancy or the perinatal period. Some common risk factors for PPA include a history of perinatal or generalized anxiety, higher-risk pregnancies, history of pregnancy loss or complications, and adverse previous childbirth experiences. Stress, isolation, and relationship conflict can increase the risk for PPA as well (Ghaedrahmati et al., 2017).

The typical signs and symptoms of PPA include:

- Intrusive thoughts
- Racing thoughts
- Difficulty concentrating
- Physical symptoms, such as heart palpitations, headaches, muscle tension, sweating, shaking, and stomachaches
- Fears about the baby's health
- Changes in appetite
- Difficulties sleeping or resting when able to
- Feeling easily overwhelmed
- Panic attacks

In contrast to PPD, in which women might detach or withdraw from their baby, those with PPA can't stop thinking about their baby. Although some level of anxiety after having a baby is common and evolutionarily appropriate, the anxiety that accompanies PPA is uncontrollable, irrational, and overwhelming. Women will often describe this anxiety as almost paralyzing because it renders them unable to function or engage in everyday activities. For example, a new mother whose baby is sleeping through the night may become so consumed with anxiety that she stares at the baby monitor all night or goes into the nursery every 10 minutes to ensure her baby is still breathing. This impacts her sleep and disrupts her ability to function in day-to-day life.

PPD	Baby Blues	PPA
Crying, sadness, or guilt	Irregular mood	Excessive worry or intrusive thoughts that something bad will happen
Irritability or anger	Feeling overwhelmed at times with adjustment to this new normal	Inability to relax
Sleeping or eating disturbances	Sleeping or eating disturbances	Sleeping or eating disturbances
Loss of interest in previously enjoyed activities	Joy, sadness, excitement, loneliness, and sometimes hopelessness	Physical symptoms (e.g., sweating, dizziness, stomach pains)

When Caitlin looks back at her own pregnancy and postpartum experience, she can say in retrospect that she *definitely* had PPA. During pregnancy, she became obsessed with counting kicks. If she hadn't noticed any for an hour or so, she would need to drink some juice and put her feet up until they came. She would also wake up like clockwork in the middle of the night and lie awake until she felt movement.

Once the baby was born, things went into overdrive. Whenever her son was napping, he would turn his face to the side and press it up against the side of the bassinet. In response, Caitlin frantically started looking for other bassinets made from mesh or other breathable material, which quickly turned into an internet rabbit hole. She started researching information and statistics on SIDS, trying to do the math in her head of the probability that it could happen to her son. When her husband came home from work one night, she started hysterically bawling that they needed to get a new bassinet. Luckily, after two to three months, these symptoms subsided, and she could actually enjoy her maternity leave.

Postpartum anxiety is vicious. Although many women are familiar with PPD, there is much less awareness around PPA, despite how debilitating it can be. If you are struggling with PPA, we encourage you to reach out to a mental health provider or other medical professional who can help you manage your intrusive thoughts through therapy or medication. We also recommend looking up online or community support groups in your area. And as with the strategies we recommended for PPD, make sure you are taking care of yourself—getting enough sleep, exercise, and nutrition.

POSTPARTUM OBSESSIVE-COMPULSIVE DISORDER

Postpartum obsessive-compulsive disorder (PP-OCD) is a perinatal mood disorder that involves recurrent, intrusive thoughts about harming the baby in some way. These intrusive thoughts (known as *obsessions*) are coupled with ritualistic behaviors that an individual performs in an attempt to get rid of the obsessions (known as *compulsions*). For example, a mother who is obsessively worried about smothering her baby may avoid doing certain tasks, like clothing or diaper changes, out of fear that she'll inadvertently act out the obsession. Although PP-OCD is not as common as some of the other perinatal mood disorders—only affecting between 3–5 percent of mothers—it can be an extremely unsettling experience to have these strange and unwanted thoughts (Carberg & Langdon, 2019).

PP-OCD can involve a variety of obsessions, many of which involve increased anxiety related to the health and safety of the baby. Here are some of the more common ones:

- Thoughts of the baby dying from SIDS
- Fear that the baby will become seriously ill
- Concerns about making decisions that will cause the baby to get hurt
- Unwanted or disturbing sexual thoughts related to the baby
- Fear of exposing the baby to harmful germs
- Images or thoughts of hurting the baby, such as dropping or throwing baby

These obsessions are often followed by compulsive behaviors to neutralize or prevent the fear from coming true. For example:

- Increased cleanliness activities, such as hand washing, showering, or bathing
- Constantly seeking reassurance from others
- Mental rituals, such as counting, reordering things, or frequent checking
- Avoidance of certain activities (e.g., changing, bathing, or carrying the baby)

Research has shown that PP-OCD emerges at higher-than-expected rates for postpartum moms, with depressed mood, poor sleep, and fatigue being predictors of more obsessive-compulsive thoughts. When you are feeling crappy and not sleeping well, you are less emotionally regulated, and you can be more susceptible to these thoughts. Typically, those with a history of OCD are at an increased risk for PP-OCD. They can also experience a worsening of symptoms that are specifically focused on their infant.

For example, Jazmin is a first-time mom who is about four months postpartum. Although she has a history of OCD that was first diagnosed in her early 20s, she has managed her symptoms for several years now. After giving birth to her son, the first few weeks went fairly smoothly, but then she noticed herself having an increase in obsessions and compulsions. She was constantly flooded with vivid images of dropping her son or finding him extremely ill. As a result, she has started frequently checking on him throughout the night and during naps. She will also wash her hands multiple times a day and frequently check food labels in the fridge to make sure she isn't eating any expired or contaminated food that she could pass on to the baby. Jazmin even struggles leaving the house or having people come over because she is afraid of exposing her son to germs. Jazmin has made an appointment with her family doctor to inquire about why her OCD symptoms have changed and increased significantly since the baby was born. She also wants to explore medication options that are safe for breastfeeding.

Intrusive Thoughts vs. OCD

It can be challenging to distinguish normal intrusive thoughts from PP-OCD because there can be overlap between the two. As new parents, you are constantly washing your hands, sanitizing bottles, and so on because there is a tiny brand-new person in the house. We don't know about you, but everything we read about illnesses and babies under two months old scared the crap out of us, so we made sure to boil *all* the pump and bottle parts.

However, the difference lies in the extent to which the thoughts are interfering with your life. Let's say you're having intrusive thoughts about your baby becoming sick, so you spend your day sanitizing pacifiers, toys, bottles, and anything else in sight. Of course, it is important to keep your baby away from people who are sick and to take the right precautions, but are you cleaning and disinfecting everything so much that it is preventing you from enjoying motherhood? Are they getting in the way of your day-to-day life? Or, to use a different example, are you having so many intrusive thoughts related to harming your baby that you've started avoiding typical parenting tasks, like bath time, diaper changes, or even simply holding your baby?

If so, then we encourage you to talk to your health care provider, as this can be a sign of PP-OCD. They can prescribe medication or give you therapy options to help with your symptoms. We encourage you to reach out to a professional trained in a type of CBT know as exposure and response prevention (ERP). This is considered the treatment of choice for OCD, and it can free you from the cycle of obsessions and compulsions interfering with your life.

If you'd like more information about intrusive thoughts and motherhood, you can refer to chapter 6 of this book, which details the new images and thoughts you may experience when you become parents.

POSTPARTUM POSTTRAUMATIC STRESS DISORDER

Postpartum posttraumatic stress disorder (PP-PTSD) is a disorder that arises due to the real or perceived experience of a life-threatening event during the perinatal period. Affecting approximately 9 to 17 percent of new mothers, it is most often experienced by those who had a chaotic, grueling, or challenging pregnancy, labor and delivery, or postpartum journey. Some of the most common risk factors for PP-PTSD include a prior history of trauma or a traumatic birth experience, which may have involved a premature birth or NICU stay, medical complications (e.g., preeclampsia or hemorrhaging), birth complications (e.g., a prolapsed umbilical cord or unplanned C-section), or medical interventions (e.g., the use of forceps or a vacuum) (Grekin & O'Hara, 2014). However, it is important to note that trauma is in the eye of the beholder. If your experience is not listed below, trauma can also be defined by you.

Here are some of the typical signs and symptoms of PP-PTSD:

- Insomnia
- Nightmares
- Reliving the past traumatic experience
- Avoidance of triggers associated with the trauma (such as the birthing hospital)
- Emotional detachment
- Difficulty connecting with your partner or child
- Grief and loss
- Anxiety
- Depression
- Self-blame for what happened
- Panic attacks

Like other forms of PTSD, the trauma associated with PP-PTSD can make you feel like you're in a constant state of fight or flight. For example, Mercedes experienced a relatively uncomplicated pregnancy and was looking forward to trying for an unmedicated vaginal birth at the hospital. However, when she went into labor with her son, she didn't progress quickly enough and needed medical intervention. When the time finally came to push, her baby's heart rate dropped, and she needed to have an emergency C-section. Her son was then taken immediately to the NICU since he had spent a brief period of time without oxygen during labor and delivery. After a few days in the NICU, Mercedes was able to take her son home, but she found herself struggling with increased anxiety and a constant need to check on the baby. She also experienced flashbacks of being rushed into the operating room, had difficulty sleeping, and had a short temper. She often found herself blaming her body for not protecting her baby and being unable to deliver the way she felt she was supposed to.

If you are struggling with symptoms of PP-PTSD, please know that these symptoms are highly treatable with the assistance of a trained health care professional. We encourage you to reach out for help to see what medication or therapy options might be right for you. Certain therapeutic approaches, like EMDR or CBT, can help you process the trauma so it no longer overwhelms you.

POSTPARTUM RAGE

People are often shocked—and also a bit relieved—to learn that it's not uncommon to experience anger, frustration, and rage during the postpartum period. Although we typically associate perinatal mood disorders with depression and anxiety, it is also possible to experience intense anger during the perinatal period, which can be directed toward yourself, your partner or family, or your kids.

Postpartum rage (or "mom rage" as we sometimes call it) can be a scary experience. You can feel disconnected from yourself and wonder what is happening, as if you are spiraling out of control. For some people, postpartum rage can involve a slow-burning anger that doesn't necessarily explode but that results in frequent feelings of unhappiness and frustration. For others, it can be more of an explosive anger, where one little thing leads to an outburst of emotion.

Here are some of the typical signs and symptoms of postpartum rage:

- Increased physical expressions of anger (e.g., yelling, slamming doors, throwing things)
- Difficulty controlling temper
- Violent thoughts or urges
- Feeling powerless to control your emotions
- Feeling overwhelmed all the time
- Intrusive thoughts
- Feelings of guilt and shame following the angry episode

Although postpartum rage is often an expression of PPD or PPA, it can also exist on its own. It can be a symptom of your needs not being met, having a lack of support, feeling isolated, or feeling overwhelmed with the day-to-day tasks of being a mom. For example, when Elizabeth's daughter was a year old, her tantrums were becoming so big that Elizabeth didn't have the capacity to manage them without becoming dysregulated herself. She found herself becoming increasingly frustrated with her child's emotional outbursts and she felt like she was living in constant chaos. It was impossible to get anything accomplished during the day, and by the time bedtime rolled around, she felt totally worn out. She found herself blowing up at her partner over seemingly inconsequential things and having the urge to scream at the top of her lungs. Afterward, she would feel like a bad wife and mother for losing control.

Postpartum Rage Is Real...

Is a warning sign or distress signal

Can make you feel powerless over your emotions

May make you feel ashamed or guilty

Is often an overlooked symptom

Means it is time to reach out for support

Is a common postpartum experience

May make you feel fearful of your anger

May be directed toward your baby, yourself, or your partner

Why Is Mom Rage Not Talked About?

Up to 35 percent of moms report feeling anger at six weeks postpartum (Colino & Fabian Weber, 2021), so why isn't postpartum rage talked about more often? Well, for starters, it can feel incredibly uncomfortable and shameful because it's seen as a contrast to the traditional mothering role. It feels so different from what you see on social media and from other parents, such as the mom cuddling with her kids or lovingly creating meals (which is just a snapshot of a moment in time and does not reflect reality). The incongruence of these images with your emotions can cause postpartum rage to build in secret, even though so many of us experience it.

However, anger is not a bad emotion. (As a matter of fact, there is no such thing as "bad" emotions. While certain emotions can be more uncomfortable, they all serve a purpose in that they're trying to tell us something.) Anger, for one, lets you know that you haven't been treated fairly or that you've been violated in some way. As therapists, we often see people coming into our office saying, "This happened, and I am so angry about it!" When we respond with "Yes, you should feel angry about that!" we will often get some confused looks. But it's true! Your anger is valid and makes sense because it's letting you know that something isn't going right in your life.

So if you are struggling with postpartum rage, don't judge your anger or push it away. In fact, suppressing your anger can actually lead to PPD. Instead, take some time to reflect on what your anger is telling you, and use it as a guide to point you out of the chaos. Do you have unmet needs? Are you experiencing a postpartum mood disorder? What is going on at that moment when you get angry? Get curious and start brainstorming about what it is that you really need.

POSTPARTUM PSYCHOSIS

Although postpartum psychosis is a relatively rare diagnosis—affecting less than 1 percent of all mothers—it is an extremely serious condition that requires immediate medical intervention. Women with postpartum psychosis represent an imminent risk of harm to themselves and their baby, and they may engage in life-threatening actions in this altered mental state. Most of the symptoms of postpartum psychosis begin rapidly and include (Bergink et al., 2015; Sit et al., 2006):

- Delusions (strange beliefs that aren't true)
- Hallucinations (seeing or hearing things that aren't there)
- Feeling irritated or agitated
- Decreased need for sleep or insomnia
- Paranoia and suspiciousness
- Rapid mood swings
- Rambling speech
- Confused thinking

Women are at highest risk for postpartum psychosis in the first month following birth, especially if they have a history of bipolar disorder or previous psychotic illness (Valdimarsdóttir et al., 2009). For example, approximately one week after delivering her daughter, Anita began behaving out of character and exhibiting some paranoid thinking. She began voicing concerns that her food was poisoned and that someone was going to steal the baby. At first, her husband thought this was related to exhaustion and lack of sleep, but her symptoms quickly worsened. She started being unable to fall asleep and refused to bathe. When she told her husband that voices were telling her to throw the baby out the window, he took her to the emergency room, where she was diagnosed with and treated for postpartum psychosis. If you or anyone you know is showing signs of this disorder, call 911 or head to your nearest emergency room.

POSTPARTUM BIPOLAR DISORDER

Although it's normal to have mood swings during the postpartum period—after all, your hormones are all over the place—for some women, these fluctuations in mood can be a sign of postpartum bipolar disorder. Affecting less than 4 percent of women, the symptoms of postpartum bipolar disorder include extreme fluctuations in mood and energy level that occur in the days and weeks following birth (Bhat et al., 2018). Women with postpartum bipolar disorder may experience moods that oscillate between the highest of highs (mania or hypomania) and the lowest of lows (depression).

While the postpartum period itself is a vulnerable time for developing mood disorders in general, some common risk factors for postpartum bipolar disorder include a history of PPD or postpartum psychosis, a personal history of bipolar disorder, or a family history of bipolar disorder, especially in first-degree relatives (Wessler et al., 2016). Although women with a history of bipolar disorder can experience a recurrence of symptoms during the perinatal period, others may experience their first bipolar episode during this time.

Similar to classic bipolar disorder, postpartum bipolar disorder can manifest as either bipolar I or bipolar II disorder. Typically, the symptoms of both types are quite similar, but in bipolar II, the changes in mood are less drastic than in bipolar I. Specifically, bipolar I is associated with intense elevations in mood that persist for over a week and that can require hospitalization (mania), whereas bipolar II involves milder changes in mood and energy that last for at least four days (hypomania). In addition, while bipolar II disorder requires the presence of both a hypomanic episode and a depressive episode, only an episode of mania is needed for a diagnosis of bipolar I disorder.

The following are some of the more specific signs and symptoms of mania versus hypomania that can be present in postpartum bipolar disorder.

The following are symptoms of mania:

- Abnormally elevated mood
- Rapid speech
- Unusually high energy
- Exaggerated sense of confidence
- Racing thoughts
- Impulsive or risky behavior
- Distractibility
- Reduced need for sleep

The following are symptoms of hypomania:

- Extremely upbeat mood
- Being more talkative or social
- Restlessness or fidgetiness
- Overconfidence
- Distractibility
- Increased productivity or creativity
- Reduced need for sleep

Postpartum bipolar disorder is often difficult to diagnose because mania and hypomania can closely mimic PPD and some normative mood changes that occur in the perinatal period (Pope et al., 2014). If you're struggling with any of the symptoms of mania or hypomania, make sure to talk to your health care provider right away so they can explore these symptoms with you. Treatment of postpartum bipolar disorder often requires the use of medication, including certain mood stabilizers, to keep you from cycling between these intense moods. Certain medications are safe to take while breastfeeding, while others are not, so you'll want to let your provider know whether or not you're nursing.

In addition, it is important to practice regular self-care if you are diagnosed with bipolar disorder at any stage of the perinatal period, as stress and sleep deprivation are two of the most common factors that can trigger episodes of mania or hypomania. Lowering your stress levels and getting a good night's sleep may sound easier said than done when you have a newborn to take care of, so reach out to your support system or look at community resources in your area. Is there a family member or friend who can assist with night feeds? How about parent playgroups that can ease the burden of being a new mom?

SUPPORTING YOUR PARTNER POSTPARTUM

If your partner is currently navigating a postpartum mood disorder and you're feeling a little lost on how to help, here are a few things we recommend:

- **Take on other household roles.** Be open to providing help, whether it's offering to do the laundry, wash dishes, or cook supper. Find what roles and responsibilities can be divided differently in the house.

- **Provide feeding support.** While bottle-feeding may not be feasible if your partner is exclusively breastfeeding, see if you can help out with feeds in other ways. For example, perhaps you can assist with nighttime feedings by changing the baby's diaper and putting the baby back to sleep when your partner is done with feeding.

- **Have moments of connection.** Relationship dynamics often change and take a back seat when a baby arrives. Try to intentionally check in with your partner throughout the day. This can be as simple as sending a text message during the day or making time for a five-minute check-in every evening. Above all, provide them with encouragement and positive feedback. Your partner may need to hear that they are doing the best that they can. Don't be afraid to share that with them.

- **Create rituals with your partner and baby.** You might begin a habit of reading, doing bath time, or putting the baby to sleep as a team. Rituals will help you bond together as a family.

- **Co-create a postpartum coping plan.** Creating a plan together will help both you and your partner feel more prepared for the postpartum period. This can also help you better recognize each other's warning signs for postpartum depression, anxiety, OCD, rage, and so on. Sometimes it can be hard to see these symptoms in yourself, so having that discussion beforehand can be helpful. Make sure this plan also includes ways to take care of your own well-being.

- **Support your partner in getting help.** Help your partner seek support, whether it's from a local provider, a support group, or an online community.

TAKEAWAYS

We know becoming a parent isn't easy! There are so many physical changes to contend with while you're raising a tiny human. Postpartum mood disorders, while relatively common, are often overlooked. We hope this chapter has provided you with some information so you feel more prepared on what symptoms to look out for. Above all, it is important to speak up and share your experiences. You *do not* have to power through it alone or wait until your symptoms go away. Reach out and get support from someone you feel comfortable being vulnerable with, whether it's your health care provider, a trained perinatal therapist, an online community, or support groups in your area. We also truly believe in the power of creating a postpartum coping plan, which is a great way to ensure that you are aware of your signs of distress and have resources on hand to help you during this time.

OUR FAVORITE RESOURCES

- Postpartum Support International (www.postpartum.net)
- Pacific Postpartum Support Society (www.postpartum.org)

16 Romantic Relationships

Sarah and Kyle arrive at couples counseling. Sarah looks like she's ready for business, but Kyle follows in behind her, looking uneasy—like he would rather be having a tooth pulled than be in a therapist's office. Sarah sits down and warmly introduces herself, while Kyle quietly sits beside her, not saying anything until Sarah gives him the side-eye and he finally introduces himself. "We are struggling so much," says Sarah. "We can't get on the same page with our parenting styles, and it is tearing us apart. I am feeling so burned out. I never thought it would be like this. We are arguing over everything, and I just feel so angry all the time. This isn't good for us, and it certainly isn't good for our kids. Sometimes we think we would be better people apart."

As psychologists, we hear from so many couples who are struggling just like Sarah and Kyle. That's because children bring so much change into the picture. Pre-kids, your life looked vastly different—there's no denying that. You could probably jump into the car at a moment's notice, drive for hours, stay up late, and sleep in the next morning without giving it a second thought. After having kids, those spontaneous trips are much trickier to achieve, staying up late often involves nighttime feedings, and sleeping in…well, we'll just leave it there.

In this chapter, we'll explore how relationships change postpartum, along with some of the unexpected issues that may arise after having a baby. We will also dive into how resentment can rear its ugly head and discuss how to make repairs when a relationship rupture does occur.

Finally, we'll take a look at the five love languages and provide you with strategies to navigate sex and intimacy in the postpartum period. We hope that by the end of this chapter, you'll have the strategies you and your partner need to find each other again after baby.

WHY IS MY RELATIONSHIP DIFFERENT?

The transition to parenthood can be one of the trickiest relationship milestones to navigate. Even if you spent nine months prepping for the baby—from the stroller to the car seat to the nursery setup—one area that so many parents are not prepared for is the shift in their relationship. Yes, things change after you get married or move in together, but nothing prepares you for the shift that happens once you became parents. Parents navigating this new role often wonder, *Who the hell are we and what the hell are we supposed to do now? Is it normal for my relationship to have changed so much?*

The answer is yes! It is normal that your relationship has changed. You have changed and your partner has changed. You left your home as a couple and came home as a family of three (or maybe even more). Making the adjustment from pre-kids to post-kids is a huge one, and this adjustment can often come with some bumps in the road. In fact, an estimated two-thirds of couples experience reduced relationship quality within the first three years of becoming parents. Oftentimes, this dissatisfaction can be a result of:

1. **Hidden expectations.** You come into parenthood with a set of expectations regarding how things will go once the baby is here. You may assume that the baby will sleep through the night within the first few weeks, that you'll still be able to get out of the house in five minutes or less, that you'll still make time for intimacy with the same frequency

that you did before, that you won't look like a hot mess most of the time, that you'll make tons of friends in the fellow "parent club"—so on and so forth. However, with the many intricacies that come with raising a kid, these expectations are inevitably not met. (How many of you still have toddlers who won't sleep through the night and find that it takes three hours to get out of the house?) As a result of these expectations not being met, frustration and resentment can begin to add up, especially when these expectations are not communicated. Take some time to explore your expectations regarding parenthood.

What are some of the expectations you had regarding your relationship in parenthood?

_____

_____

_____

_____

How do you communicate your expectations with your partner?

_____

_____

_____

_____

Are these expectations realistic for where you are in your parenting journey? Why or why not?

_____

_____

_____

_____

2. **Increased responsibilities.** Before you have kids, you often have a lot of unspoken rules or assumptions about who will be the "boss" of the house and make decisions concerning the kids, housework, meal preparation, or finances. These rules often come from the way you were raised as children. Just think back to your own childhood: Did your mom always do the cooking and cleaning? Did your dad always take care of the vehicles and the finances? If you grew up in a single-parent household, does it just seem natural to just take on everything because that's what was modeled to you as a child?

    Many times, unspoken rules can be a source of conflict when there isn't clear communication about who is doing what. This is a common theme with many of the parents we see in our practice, especially among parents just trying to survive those early months postpartum. Many of these parents tell us that if they could go back in time, they would more evenly divide the duties and responsibilities.

    Even if you have kids that are older, that's okay—you can still figure out how to divvy up your responsibilities in a way that works for you as a couple. Your job is to work together. Not to fuse together as one, but to complement each other's thoughts, feelings, strengths, and weaknesses.

What are your current roles and responsibilities?

_____

_____

_____

_____

What responsibilities do you hate and want to do as little as possible?

_____

_____

_____

_____

What responsibilities can you take on more of?

_____

_____

_____

_____

What are your partner's current roles and responsibilities?

_____

_____

_____

_____

What responsibilities does your partner hate and want to do as little as possible of?

_____

_____

_____

_____

What responsibilities can your partner take on more of?

_____

_____

_____

_____

3. **Potential resentment.** The initial transition into parenthood can be such a high-risk time for relationships. Resentment can start to build up if we're taking on too much, not setting healthy boundaries for ourselves, not making time for intimacy and sex, and not getting our needs met. It's essentially a build-up that occurs when you continue putting yourself last all the time!

Resentment can also come from within yourself. For example, let's say that your partner hasn't been picking up after themselves lately and it's driving you up the wall. You may start to personalize this behavior and believe that they are doing it because they are selfish, they don't respect you, or they don't believe you are working hard enough. Soon you only interpret your partner's behaviors through this negative lens. The problem with this cognitive bias is that you are always looking for evidence that confirms your belief. *Yep, there are dirty dishes in the sink again. My partner really doesn't give a shit about me.* If you continue to let this build up, it can soon start affecting many aspects of your relationship.

To start tackling resentment in your relationship, first ask yourself what specifically you are becoming resentful about. Is it that your partner is sleeping all night while you are up with baby? Is it that they're not helping out with day-to-day tasks around the house? Is it that they get to go on business trips without you, leaving you at home with a baby all week long? Then ask yourself what you can let go of and what behaviors truly need to change to get your needs met in the relationship.

What actions or inactions from your partner trigger resentment for you?

_____

_____

_____

_____

What things can you let go of (e.g., dirty dishes in the sink, a mess in the bathroom)?

_____

_____

_____

_____

What things need to change (e.g., help with nighttime feedings, making time for intimacy)?

_____

_____

_____

_____

Resentment in Parenthood Can Come From...

Lack of support

Carrying the mental load alone

Longing for authentic connection

Comparing your struggles to others' struggles

Difficulties feeling heard and validated

Thoughts about your body

Feeling disrespected or having boundaries violated

Difficulty balancing your role as a parent

CHANGING HOW YOU COMMUNICATE

Before we go any further in helping you navigate your relationship postpartum, we want you to start by simply acknowledging that your relationship is different from how it used to be. How often do you just stop to acknowledge that life after kids is just so different? We know that parents rarely do, usually because there is just so much to do, especially in those first few months, and they really don't even consider it once it becomes routine. But when you acknowledge that things feel different—that your relationship feels different—you can finally develop the awareness needed to break your negative patterns of interacting. You can become aware of errors in how you communicate—or fail to communicate. You can become aware of when you're kind and open versus when you're blaming or shaming. You must first cultivate this awareness and then make a commitment to change your relationship patterns.

Let's return to Sarah and Kyle's example from the start of this chapter. Sarah sits on the couch and talks about being home all day with the kids. "They are just so tough to keep entertained. I am trying to keep them busy, but as soon I bring out one activity, they make a mess, decide they are done, and then go off to do another thing. Then I am left to clean everything up and chase after them still. My day feels like endless running around in circles to keep up with them and to keep the house from looking like a war zone." By the time Kyle comes home from work, Sarah is usually fuming, and it's overwhelming for him to know that he's going to walk into hostility almost every day. "I usually end up retreating," Kyle says, "because I don't know what the hell to do."

This is the perfect breeding ground for resentment. To avoid this resentment and change their pattern of interacting, Sarah and Kyle first need to have a level of empathy and understanding for what each person is going through. Then they need to make their needs known to each other. Often, this starts with open communication. Although this is such a simple solution, we see many couples wait until things are in the danger zone before they take a long, hard look at how they communicate.

The key to sharing your feelings is to use I-statements, which communicate your needs without shame or blame. This is in contrast to you-statements (i.e., those phrases that begin with "You never..." or "You always..."), which will almost certainly get a defensive response from your partner. An I-statement template might look like this:

I feel ___*state the emotion*___ when ___*explain the situation*___ because ___*describe why this matters to you*___. Would you ___*state specifically what you want*___?

To change their pattern of interacting, Sarah can practice using I-statements with Kyle when he gets home from work. This part of the day seems to be a high-risk time for them, as Sarah is typically feeling burned out and Kyle is feeling anxious. A different dialogue for Kyle and Sarah may look like this:

Sarah: "I feel overwhelmed when I'm home with the kids all day because I never get a break. Would you be able to help with Bella's five o'clock feeding?"

Kyle: "Ah, it sounds like you had a rough day. Sure, take a break upstairs while I feed Bella."

Sarah: "Thanks, I really appreciate you giving me this time. I know you are probably needing a break as well."

Remember, you need to make your needs known because other people can't read your mind. You can use the following exercise to get into the habit of using I-statements with your partner.

Exercise
Using I-Statements

I-statements can help you share your feelings in a calm, explanatory fashion. By thinking about what you really need from the other person and discussing it with them—instead of demanding they make changes—you can let them know why your need is important to you. We have provided an example first, followed by space to practice writing your own.

Step 1: Identify the need that you want to make known.

> I need you to help with nighttime feedings

Step 2: Turn it into an I-statement.

I feel _____ when _____ because _____. Would you _____?

> I feel overworked when you sleep the entire night because I am waking up for every feeding. Would you take turns with me getting up with the baby?

Step 1: Identify the need that you want to make known.

_____

_____

_____

Step 2: Turn it into an I-statement.

_____

_____

_____

Step 1: Identify the need that you want to make known.

_____

_____

_____

Step 2: Turn it into an I-statement.

_____

_____

_____

Step 1: Identify the need that you want to make known.

_____

_____

_____

Step 2: Turn it into an I-statement.

_____

_____

_____

Step 1: Identify the need that you want to make known.

_____

_____

_____

Step 2: Turn it into an I-statement.

_____

_____

_____

RUPTURE AND REPAIR WITH YOUR KIDS

We fought in front of our kids. Are we stuck with a lifetime therapy bill? As a couple, it is inevitable that you will have disagreements and not always get along. The key, though, is to have assertive discussions and model healthy ways to deal with conflict for your kids.

Children take in so much more than what you recognize and give them credit for, even when they're very young. Some parents we've worked with have told us that they "fought a lot" when their kids were really young but that "the kids were too young to remember it, so it's fine." Unfortunately, this cannot be further from the truth! In fact, young children demonstrate increased levels of cortisol in response to parental fighting, meaning that their stress hormones are going on overdrive, even if they can't express their feelings to you. Because of this, you want to model for you children how to disagree with another person while still showing love and respect. It is okay to bring up concerns in an assertive manner, but you want to avoid blaming, shaming, and name-calling.

In addition, you want to model how to make repairs when a rupture does occur. So often, parents get into arguments and then pretend like nothing happened. All of a sudden, they are getting along and laughing again, so there was a repair that happened somewhere along the line, but the kids have no idea what happened. They witnessed the fight but never witnessed the repair. This is so confusing to kids because all they see is that their parents were so angry and then—boom—everything is back to normal. On top of that, it doesn't teach kids any conflict resolution skills or show them what to do with those angry feelings.

You want to give your kids the story of what happened *and* allow them to witness the repair by following these simple steps:

1. **Narrate what happened.** "You probably heard Mommy and Daddy using loud voices. That probably felt scary."

2. **Describe the repair.** "Sometimes grownups get angry, just like you do sometimes, but we shouldn't have yelled. We love each other and have talked it out using kinder words. We want you to know that what we were talking about is not your fault. We will always be able to take care of you, and we are still having dinner together as a family in a couple of hours." You can always add more context and narrative depending on your child's age.

NAVIGATING MATERNAL GATEKEEPING

How many of you have had the opportunity to have an open and honest conversation about what you want your parenting style to look like? Typically, most people go into parenthood with their own set of values and beliefs without having an explicit conversation about this with their partner. This can backfire quickly when you and your partner disagree about how to best handle a particular issue with your child. Chances are, you'll be thinking, *I am right. I know how to do right by our kids. I am a good parent*—and your partner will be thinking the exact same thing.

When you do this as a mother, you can fall into the trap of maternal gatekeeping, which occurs when you insist that your partner do things the way *you* do them or the way that you determine is best. This can lead your partner to feel anxious or insecure in their role because they're afraid that they'll do it "wrong."

Sarah struggled *big time* with maternal gatekeeping with one of her kids. Whenever her partner was in charge of changing their son's diaper, she was very critical of how he would hold up the baby's legs: "You are not being gentle enough" or "You need to only hold his legs up this high." Or whenever the baby would cry when her partner was rocking him to sleep, she would chime in and say, "Here, just let me do it. You're doing it wrong." But how was he doing it wrong? (Spoiler alert: He wasn't! It was just wrong according to Sarah.)

What Sarah needed to do in that moment was trust in her partner's ability to perform tasks related to the baby in a way that he was comfortable with. As humans, we are all very different people, and we are inherently going to do things differently. And that is okay! To combat maternal gatekeeping, you need to start by acknowledging that you and your partner are different people with two different upbringings, values, and beliefs.

Then give your partner the space to do what they need to do. Resist the urge to jump in and take over (unless it's a safety concern, of course). Whenever you're tempted to take control, just notice where you feel the urge in your body. It's okay to have uncomfortable feelings. Tolerating discomfort means you are exhibiting movement and growth. Then ask yourself if you can stay present and manage the urge to take control. If so, then stay present. If not, then leave the room and go do something else!

For example, let's say your partner is feeding your six-month-old baby, and there is puréed food coating the entire room from the highchair to the ceiling. All you want to do is jump in and show your partner how to do it the "right" way, but you catch yourself in the middle of this urge. You notice that you are feeling anxious and frustrated about the mess. At this point, you ask yourself whether your partner's feeding style is a safety concern. The answer here is no. Your partner's feeding style, while admittedly messy, is doing nothing to hurt your baby. (Now if your partner was giving your baby hard carrots, then *yes*, you'd want to say something! Always say something about safety concerns.)

Next, you ask yourself if you can control the urge to take charge of the situation. If you can't, walk away! We know how hard it is to let go when you have the urge to fix things to make them "better"—speaking from our own gatekeeping experience—but you can do it.

Ultimately, it is important to recognize that we all have different strengths and weaknesses as parents. You cannot expect your partner to parent the exact same way as you because you are different people with different life experiences. Despite these differences, know that you share one common value: You want the best for your children. You want to raise them with self-esteem and resiliency. So although you won't always agree with how your partner handles parenting tasks, it's okay. You can still be a united front.

Use the following exercises to help you recognize how differences in parenting can cause disagreements—and how to resolve conflict with simple connection.

Exercise
Considering Your Parenting Styles

You and your partner will differ, and maybe even argue, on some aspects of parenting. It's likely to cause a disagreement (or two or three or four) along the way. This partly comes from all those outside sources—how your own parents raised you, influences from other people in your life, and even information you've picked up about parenting. It's important to recognize the differences between you and your partner's parenting styles and where they may have originated. Remember, the ultimate goal is not to be right—it's to provide the best for your child.

How would you describe your parenting style?

_____

_____

_____

_____

How would you describe your partner's parenting style?

_____

_____

_____

_____

_____

How were you parented while growing up? How does that reflect in your parenting now?

_____

_____

_____

_____

_____

How was your partner parented while growing up? How does that reflect in their parenting now?

_____

_____

_____

_____

_____

What are some aspects of your parenting style that you are not willing to change?

_____

_____

_____

_____

What are some aspects of your partner's parenting style that you are willing to adopt?

_____

_____

_____

_____

_____

Exercise
Learning Your Partner's Love Language

One of the most effective ways to move from conflict to connection is to learn your partner's love language. Introduced by Dr. Gary Chapman (2010), the concept of the love language is that we all have different ways that we enjoy receiving love and affection. Once we know our love language and that of our partner, we can see the "why" behind some of their actions or inactions. Here are the five love languages, with some examples of each:

1. **Acts of service.** For some people, actions speak louder than words. Individuals with this love language appreciate it when their partner goes out of their way to make things easier for them. This is definitely Caitlin's love language! She loves it whenever her husband makes her coffee in the morning, helps with meal prep, and does the laundry.

2. **Quality time.** Some people feel the most connected when they're able to spend uninterrupted one-on-one time together with their partner. That means getting off the phone or computer and really giving the gift of quality, undivided attention.

3. **Receiving gifts.** People with this love language value receiving gifts from their partner, whether it's a homemade card or a box of chocolates. The gift doesn't need to be elaborate or come with a hefty price tag—it's the thought that counts.

4. **Words of affirmation.** Some people value verbal acknowledgments of affection, including compliments, words of encouragement, and "I love yous." When someone values words of affirmations, it's easy to make their day by leaving a

simple love note on the fridge or sending a random thinking-of-you text in the middle of the day.

5. **Physical touch.** Those with this love language feel loved when their partner demonstrates physical signs of affection, which can include holding hands, cuddling, kissing, or having sex. For these individuals, a simple cuddle session or shoulder rub can go a long way at the end of a hard day.

What is your love language? _____

What is your partner's love language? _____

What can you do more of that reflects your partner's love language? What can you do less of?

_____

_____

_____

_____

What can your partner do more of that reflects your love language? What can your partner do less of?

_____

_____

_____

_____

_____

POSTPARTUM INTIMACY

We may talk about our birth stories—what went well and what did not go well—but how often do we talk about what it's like to have sex for the first time after childbirth? Some women avoid having sex postpartum because they are scared it will be painful. Others jump right into it and are taken aback if they encounter pain during the experience, which turns them off to the idea of sex for months. Both are equally stressful experiences. Although having a direct conversation about sex can be uncomfortable, what's more uncomfortable is having sex before your body and mind are ready. In this section, we'll explore how to reframe thoughts about sex, navigate lack of sexual desire, and create feelings of togetherness.

Reframing Thoughts About Sex

So many of us view sex as a relational chore, which can make it easy to keep putting it off until later. You might think, *I simply don't have it in me. I am so tired. I've had kids touching me all day.* When you think of sex as just another thing that you need to check off at the end of a long day, it can take the pleasure and connection out of it. And before you know it, resentment can develop between partners. To rekindle your love life, you want to reframe your thoughts around sex so you view it as a relational and connecting experience rather than a purely physical one. You also want to take ownership over your sex life. Instead of thinking, *I'm only doing this for you. This is just one more box I need to check off on my huge list of things to do*, allow yourself to be a sexual being with specific wants and needs.

What are your current thoughts about sex (e.g., It's just one more thing to do, I don't have enough energy)?

_____

_____

_____

_____

_____

How can you reframe these thoughts to view sex as a mutually pleasurable way to feel connected with your partner (e.g., I am deciding to have sex because I deserve to have pleasure as well)?

_____

_____

_____

_____

_____

_____

Spontaneous vs. Responsive Desire

Before having kids, you may have been able to be intimate with your partner whenever you wanted—in the morning, the middle of the day, or at night. It often didn't matter, as nobody else was going to hear you or barge into your bedroom. But after having kids, your sex life can change drastically, and many couples worry that their sex life will never recover. However, knowing the difference between spontaneous and responsive sexual desire can help get things back on track.

Spontaneous desire is the sudden and intense desire for sex that precedes any actual stimulation or physical arousal. That means that the mental desire to have sex comes before you actually start being intimate with your partner. This is the type of desire that you likely had when you first came together as a couple. However, this type of desire typically fades across time as the relationship goes on. It is often replaced with responsive desire, in which the desire for sex occurs *after* you experience some sort of pleasurable sexual stimulation, such as touching or kissing. With responsive desire, physical arousal precedes mental desire.

Although both spontaneous and responsive desire are completely normal, research has shown that most women experience responsive desire. That means that if you struggle to get "turned on" at the drop of a hat, there is nothing wrong with you. It just means that intimacy is something that needs to be nurtured, whether it involves asking your partner for a massage, having a shower together, or kissing and touching.

Now that you understand the difference between spontaneous and responsive desire, see if you can figure out where you fall on the spectrum so you can let your partner know what you need to get in the mood. You deserve to have a fulfilling sex life!

What are some ways you can build up your natural sexual responses? Does it involve sending selfies in the middle of the day to let your partner know you are thinking of them? Watching erotic content together? What gets your libido going?

_____

_____

_____

_____

_____

Creating Togetherness

Some women continue to experience unexplained pain during intercourse long after they have healed from childbirth. This can involve cramping, muscle tightness, burning, or aching during or after intercourse. Known as *dyspareunia*, this condition can make it difficult to achieve sexual intimacy and can pose challenges to a couple's sexual relationship. The specific treatment for dyspareunia will depend on the symptoms and the underlying source of the pain, but it often includes medication (if there is an infection), estrogen or sexual lubricants (if there is vaginal dryness), counseling (if emotional issues are the underlying cause), or pelvic floor physiotherapy.

You can reduce the pain associated with dyspareunia by making changes to your sexual behavior and trying alternative activities to sexual intercourse while you recover. There are a variety of other ways to create intimacy and a feeling of togetherness beyond vaginal intercourse. This can include sensual massages, sexual touching, oral sex, and mutual masturbation. It can also involve small moments throughout the day where you feel a sense of closeness (e.g., holding hands, snuggling).

If you are struggling with dyspareunia, what are some other ways you can achieve intimacy in your relationship for the time being? How can you create feelings of togetherness in ways that don't involve sexual intercourse?

_____

_____

_____

_____

_____

ATTACHMENT STYLES AND YOUR RELATIONSHIP

The basic premise of attachment theory is that we all have different styles of relating with others, and these styles formed as a result of our experiences with our early caregivers. Developed by John Bowlby and Mary Ainsworth, attachment theory was revolutionary in helping us recognize the importance of early childhood relationships on future development. Prior to their research and findings, it was commonly believed that infants only relied on their mother for food and that parents should avoid giving infants too much attention. Yikes! It is astounding how much research can change generations. We wonder how long parents heeded this ill-informed advice and kept their infants at an arm's length.

So why is knowing about attachment styles important when it comes to relationships? Well, for starters, your attachment style informs how you tend to deal with rejection and conflict (as well as how your partner tends to do so). Depending on what attachment style you may have, you may shut down, demand attention, disengage, or become overly clingy in the face of an argument. Let's break down the four main attachment styles here.

SECURE ATTACHMENT

As a child, you had a caregiver who was responsive and met your needs in a balanced way. As a result:

- Your friendships are trusting and positive.
- You are flexible in relationships.
- You feel good in relationships.
- You know that, for the most part, people are reliable.

AVOIDANT ATTACHMENT

As a child, your caregiver may have been emotionally unavailable and unresponsive. As a result:

- You don't trust others easily.
- You fear rejection.
- You often check out and isolate when things become tough.
- You don't share what you're feeling.

ANXIOUS ATTACHMENT

As a child, your caregiver may have been responsive sometimes and uninvolved other times. They also may have relied on you to fulfill their needs. As a result:

- You're clingy in relationships.
- You doubt your own feelings.
- You have difficulty communicating your needs.
- You need constant reassurance that your partner loves you and won't leave.

DISORGANIZED ATTACHMENT

As a child, you may have grown up in an environment where you weren't physically or emotionally safe. As a result:

- You want to be close but often push people away.
- Your moods change rapidly.
- Your relationships tend to be chaotic and short-lived.
- You have frequent and unpredictable outbursts.

Understanding your attachment style can help you learn what you need to do to feel safe and secure within your relationship. For example, if you have an avoidant attachment style, it will be important to learn how to share your emotions and turn toward your partner (rather than turn away) in moments of conflict. If you have an anxious attachment style, you'll want to learn how to self-soothe the separation anxiety that comes up within relationships. These changes can certainly be difficult to make, as you've likely been used to acting one way for a long time and must now be cognizant of your behavior as it's occurring. It may be beneficial to discuss this with a mental health professional if you feel you need support. For those of you with a disorganized attachment style, we encourage working with a professional to help you work through the trauma and fear of your past to prevent the cycle from repeating itself.

The following are some additional tips that can help you better navigate your relationship with your partner depending on your attachment style.

TIPS FOR STRENGTHENING ATTACHMENT

Avoidant: If you shut down and disengage in your relationship, here are some tips to help you turn to your partner in moments of conflict rather than pushing them away:

- Notice the alarm bells you feel when someone gets close. Practice noticing and naming any emotions that arise for you in these moments. This is the first step when figuring out your needs.

- Communicate these needs with your partner. It's much easier for your partner to meet these needs if they know what they are in the first place.

- Practice gratitude in your relationship. Every day, take some time to focus on one thing in your relationship that are you grateful for.

- Whenever you need space, let your partner know and tell them when you will be back.

Anxious: If you struggle with space, distance, and the constant need for reassurance, here are some tips to help you feel less insecure in your relationship:

- Know what you value and desire in your relationship—and communicate, communicate, communicate this to your partner. Be clear about what you want and need to feel safe.

- Avoid faking a "That's cool, I don't care" attitude. As much as you think it will help keep your partner around, you cannot sustain an inauthentic version of yourself.

- Get into the habit of practicing mindfulness. This will help you ground yourself in moments of conflict instead of letting yourself go into fight-or-flight mode when you feel even the smallest hint of perceived rejection.

Disorganized: If you tend to run both hot and cold in your relationship, making it chaotic and unpredictable, here are some tips to help you break the pattern and deal with the unresolved trauma of your past:

- Keep track of the triggers that cause you to become dysregulated so you can catch them early on before you explode. This may involve taking some space in the midst of the argument before it escalates.

- Find a few go-to coping strategies that calm your nervous system when you are activated (e.g., deep breathing, tapping, taking a shower).

- Practice challenging the inner critic in your mind. Whenever this critical voice pops into your head, ask yourself, "What is the evidence this is true?"

- Practice communicating assertively with your partner, instead of using blaming or shaming language when you are angry. Here is where I-statements can be incredibly useful in communicating your needs and increasing the likelihood that they will get met.

HOW TO KEEP YOUR CONNECTION

Even while repairing your relationship and reconnecting with your partner, it can be easy to fall into old habits. This is especially the case for couples in the thick of managing the demands of kids, jobs, and the busyness of life. Dr. Sue Johnson (2019), the founder of a well-known therapy model called Emotionally Focused Couples Therapy, discusses the importance of the acronym *ARE* in keeping that connection:

Accessibility: Are you accessible to your partner? Are you available to talk after the kids have gone to bed, or do you do your own thing? Are you present when you spend time with them, or are you on your phone or watching your own TV show? How can you be more accessible?

_____

_____

_____

_____

Responsiveness: Are you responsive to your partner when they open up? Are you able to put down what you are doing and provide a listening ear? Do you provide words of encouragement when they let you know how things are going for them? Or is it too dysregulating for you when they open up? How can you better respond when your partner reaches out?

_____

_____

_____

_____

Engagement: Do you show your love for your partner through words, actions, and time spent together? Often, this is a tricky one for many couples. Many people assume their partner knows how much they care, when the other person is actually thinking, _I really don't know if they value me. Sometimes I question how much they truly care._ How can you let your partner know that you value them?

_____

_____

_____

_____

TAKEAWAYS

There is so much change that happens to your relationship when babies come into the picture. You have to cope with this new parent role, work through intimacy challenges, and figure out roles and responsibilities. Although these changes are inevitable, we hope this chapter has given you some practical strategies to help you shift out of resentment, communicate your needs, and find a sense of togetherness again.

OUR FAVORITE RESOURCES

- Love After Baby with Sheina Shochet, MA (www.loveafterbaby .com; Instagram: @loveafterbaby)

- Tracy Dalgleish, CPsych (www.drtracyd.com; Instagram: @drtracyd)

- My Love Thinks with Morgan Cutlip, PhD (www.mylovethinks .com/drmorgan; Instagram: @drmorgancutlip)

- *The Case for the Only Child: Your Essential Guide* by Susan Newman

17 Returning to Work

So many mothers we talk to question their readiness to return to work. It can feel like there is no perfect time to go back, especially when there are complicating factors involved, such as the need to return for financial reasons or lack of access to maternity leave. Others describe needing to return to work because they want to get that part of their identity back. No matter where you fall on this spectrum, returning to work can evoke a variety of emotions, both positive and negative, that result in inner conflict and confusion. We often hear how mothers feel torn in so many different directions. If this is your experience, it is important to know that there is no right way to feel as you go through this process. The decision to return (or not return) to work can be messy and complicated.

For example, over the past year, Sylvia has been working for a company in Canada that provides benefits to employees, including maternity leave. Sylvia had her first baby about 11 months ago and is taking a total of one year away from work, with a portion of her wage being continued over this time. Sylvia considers herself to be extremely fortunate to take this time off with her child, but with one month left in her leave, she has begun to feel a mixture of emotions about going back. On the one hand, she is excited to reconnect with her colleagues, relieve some financial pressure by getting her full wages back, and have her daughter connect with peers in daycare. On the other hand, she is feeling guilty for putting her child in someone else's care and is worried about missing out on moments of her daughter's life. Sylvia doesn't know if she is ready to go back.

Or consider the case of Nadine, who is nine months pregnant and working full-time at the same job she has had for the last five years. While her company does provide maternity leave, it is all unpaid, so for the past year, Nadine has been saving up her vacation days. She had hoped to accrue enough paid time off to spend a few weeks at home with her baby because, as a single mom, she cannot afford to lose her only source of income. However, in between all the prenatal doctor's appointments and the unexpected emergencies that have popped up, Nadine has only been able to accumulate about one week's worth of paid time off. Five days after returning from the hospital, Nadine has no choice but to return to work if she wants to be able to pay her bills. Her body hasn't even finished healing and she is racked with overwhelming feelings of grief, guilt, and anger as she returns to her job.

Does either of these stories sound familiar to you? In this chapter, we will take a look at some of the emotional experiences that can arise when returning to work after having a baby. We will provide you with a return-to-work coping plan and help you reflect on your values and practice setting work-life boundaries before you embark on your return-to-work journey.

WHAT DOES MATERNITY LEAVE LOOK LIKE?

What does maternity leave look like? This is a common question for which we unfortunately don't have the answer. Some mothers feel like their maternity leave ends too soon, some feel like it's too long, and some don't even have the luxury of a maternity leave. To make things a bit more complicated, every country typically has their own standards when it comes to the length of government-mandated maternity leave, which can vary from a few weeks to over a year. For example, countries like Estonia, Japan, Austria, and Norway all offer more than a year of paid leave, while the United States is the only industrialized nation in the world where employers are not required to offer any paid leave whatsoever (Livingston & Thomas, 2019). For us here in Alberta, the typical maternity leave is 12 to 18 months, with a percentage of your wage being provided to you during that time.

The situation gets a little more complicated for fathers, as paternity leave is still not well-recognized in many countries, and many new fathers have no options for leave available to them. We've heard from so many mothers whose partners were expected to be back at work the weekend after their baby was born, leaving the burden of caretaking to fall on the woman. It is cultural and societal practices like this that perpetuate the mental load of motherhood, as women are expected to assume the role of the default parent. While paternity leave is starting to gain more traction, it can lead to a variety of challenges for fathers, adoptive parents, or families with differing family structures. There is a lot more that needs to be done for families when they are bringing home a baby.

The following exercise will help you and your partner consider your needs and preferences for maternity leave.

Exercise
Maternity Leave Planning

If you are expecting a child (or even in the early stages of family planning) and wondering what maternity leave will look like for you, we highly recommend looking into what your employer offers. Here are some questions to consider that may be helpful for you. By asking these questions in advance, you can prepare for your particular situation as best as you can.

What type of leave is offered by your employer? For example, what is the length of time you can take off? Is the leave paid or unpaid? Are there any health benefits provided?

_____

_____

_____

Are there any financial considerations to make? For example, if the leave is paid, what wage level can you expect? Are your maternity leave payments taxable? If the leave is unpaid, does your employer have a short-term disability policy that allows you to receive a portion of your income?

_____

_____

_____

Is there a procedure for submitting paperwork to go on maternity leave? Do you need to go through your human resources department or a third party, such as an unemployment agency?

_____

_____

_____

If you have a partner or spouse, are they able to take time off as well? If you are hoping to take time off together, does your partner need to use vacation days or take a leave of absence? Or does their employer offer paternity leave?

_____

_____

_____

Does your employer have a return-to-work procedure? For example, do you need to set things up within a certain amount of time before you return? Can you plan a gradual return to work that isn't immediately full-time?

_____

_____

_____

361

THE MIXED EMOTIONS IN RETURNING TO WORK

Whether you're a first-time mom or a seasoned mom with multiple kids, it is normal to feel a host of overwhelming emotions when it comes to returning to work after you give birth. These emotions can include fear, excitement, guilt, self-doubt, loneliness, and even happiness. If you've been feeling the push and pull between these emotions, know that your experience is like so many others. There are so many factors that contribute to the return-to-work experience, so let's dive into some that might be important for you to consider.

Perhaps one of the biggest reasons why you may be experiencing mixed emotions in returning to work is that your priorities have shifted since becoming a mom. You may no longer feel the same fulfillment from your job and believe that your calling is to focus on your role as a mother, rather than constantly burning the midnight oil at work. Similarly, if you are still in that early postpartum phase, work may be the last thing on your mind when you are trying to navigate life with an infant. Because let's be honest, this period of motherhood can be absolute chaos at times. Some days you might not know what way is up, and you might feel pulled in a million different directions. Just when you think you have it figured out, they change the game on you all over again. If you are privileged to have a longer maternity leave, you may feel like you are just coming out of that postpartum fog and only beginning to enjoy different aspects of motherhood. It can be hard to return to work when you've just started to feel like you have a rhythm or have discovered parts of yourself again.

Returning to work can also involve a significant push and pull when there are financial concerns to consider, especially if you are the main or sole breadwinner for your family. In these cases, it can feel like you

Mixed Emotions When Returning to Work

Fear

Self-doubt

Happiness

Guilt

Excitement

Overwhelm

Constant push-pull between positive and negative

Loneliness

have no choice but to return to work as soon as possible in order to pay your bills. However, with the return to work comes the need for childcare, which can be extremely expensive and difficult for families to afford. This can make the return to work feel like a double-edged sword, and it sometimes makes more financial sense to not put your child into daycare. While some families have attempted to circumvent this issue by finding forms of employment that allow them to work from home, the reality is that it is near impossible to juggle working and child-rearing at the same time. It can also feel difficult for families who choose to have one parent become a stay-at-home parent when they don't necessarily want to. (And to be clear, being a stay-at-home parent is a full-time job in its own right.) Financial considerations aside, when daycare becomes a necessity, it can be difficult for parents to have their children cared for by someone else, which only adds to the conflicting emotions they are experiencing.

In addition to financial concerns, we must look at returning to work from a physical standpoint. Many mothers are still healing from the physical injury of childbirth when they go back to work. This can include mothers who gave birth via C-section and who just passed the six-week recovery period, as well as mothers who are still healing from a traumatic vaginal birth. There may also be a variety of feeding considerations to keep in mind, as a mom may need to create a breastmilk stash or learn how to pump while at work. Then there are all the hormonal fluctuations that occur during the postpartum period. For mothers experiencing a perinatal mood disorder, this only adds a layer of complexity to the mix. They may be working through a diagnosis, trying to seek therapeutic support, or struggling with their mental health on a day-to-day basis. The need to return to work can feel like an additional hurdle to overcome.

Finally, relationship dynamics can impact the mixed emotions involved in returning to work, particularly when it comes to the division of labor. For example, if you and your partner both work outside of the home but you are still the default parent who maintains most of the duties at home, it can feel extremely overwhelming to take care of everything. It can also be difficult for parents to find a new normal in their relationship when they are already trying to find a new normal with their infant. In addition, single parents, or parents with limited to no support, may feel as though they are unsure how to juggle all the roles.

Given these various factors at play, it is no wonder that there are complex emotions involved when returning to work! Just know that there is no right way to feel in this situation. For most parents, nothing feels like it's 100 percent the right decision either way. You can feel torn in multiple directions, with there never being an ideal time to return to work.

For example, Chelsea didn't really get maternity leave with her first child, as she is self-employed. This was complicated by the fact that her son came 12 weeks early, so she didn't have a plan for her clients, nor was she able to save up the amount she wanted to in order to take time off. On top of all that, she was relocated three hours away from home while her son was hospitalized in the NICU. Luckily, she had some support and understanding. Some clients were able to wait to see her until she returned to work, and for those who needed more support, some wonderful colleagues stepped in to help during the interim. Once Chelsea's son was out of the NICU, she slowly returned to working more hours. However, having a baby in NICU rocks your world, and it brought up lots of conflicting emotions when it came to her job. She wanted to be there for her son but still felt the pull of making sure her clients were supported. On top of that, she needed to make sure all her bills were covered.

During Chelsea's second maternity leave, she decided to take three months off before returning to work. Her daughter was not born prematurely, so she had an opportunity to save what she needed so she could take her time. After a few months, she decided to return to work in a limited capacity, as she has found that having some work provides her with the opportunity to feel more of a balance with motherhood. She is also lucky enough to have a support system that can care for her children. It still wasn't easy returning to work—sometimes that guilt or questioning voice still arises—but she hoped she was making the best decision she could for her family.

As Chelsea's story illustrates, returning to work can bring up a variety of complicated questions and conflicting emotions. You may find your values have changed entirely once your baby is born. If looking at your values makes you realize that your priorities in life have shifted, and perhaps returning to work no longer fits with your identity as a mother, this gives you something else to consider as well. Some consider it a privilege to stay at home with their children—and having the financial means to do so is a privilege in its own right—while others find that being at work is an important part of their identity. Everyone's journey looks different, but one thing is certain: Being a stay-at-home parent and a working parent both have value and meaning. While these two parent groups are often pitted against each other in terms of who is more important, we want to emphasize is that neither is better than the other. Both jobs are demanding and both have value.

Use the prompts here to reflect on your own return-to-work journey, knowing that it is perfectly normal to feel any emotions that may arise.

What type of conflicting emotions have you experienced when you think about returning to work? For example, perhaps you're excited to spend some time with adults, but at the same time, you're sad to be missing out on a part of your child's life.

_____

_____

_____

_____

If there were options, would you choose to stay at home with your children or would you return to your place of work?

_____

_____

If you do not have any other choice but to return to work, what thoughts or emotions come up for you?

_____

_____

_____

_____

How are these thoughts or emotions impacting your day-to-day life? Is it interfering with your ability to enjoy the time together you have with your baby right now? Is it causing conflict with your partner?

_____

_____

_____

_____

If you are returning to work, how can you create new moments of connection with your child? If you are away from your child more often, you can still find ways to connect. Even 15 minutes of undivided attention (that means no phones, no work, no distractions) during the day can have a big impact.

_____

_____

_____

_____

When you're experiencing this roller-coaster of emotions, it can be helpful to remind yourself of the values that drew you into the workforce in the first place. This can provide you with a source of grounding and comfort as you navigate the mixed feelings you have about returning to work. By considering the reasons why your job is important to you and how it benefits your life, you may feel some strength in returning to work.

How does your job add value to your life? What need does it fulfill?

_____

_____

_____

_____

BALANCING ACT

It can be difficult to find a new routine once you return to work. You might be juggling daycare drop-offs, sneaking in time to pump breastmilk between meetings, and figuring out how to knock everything off your to-do list so you don't need to stay in the office after hours. On top of it all, your parents or friends may give you a guilt trip for going back to work and not understand why you would "choose" to leave your child. It truly is a balancing act that can take some adjustment before you find your groove.

Because there is so much to juggle when it comes to navigating life as a working mom, one of the most important things you can do during this time is set boundaries at work. Be straightforward with your boss about what is (and isn't) feasible for you. If you need to leave the office every day at 4:00 p.m. to pick up your child at daycare, make this clear so they can schedule meetings earlier in the day. If there are roles or responsibilities that need to change, such as your availability for work-related travel, makes this known as well. If you don't communicate these expectations, your colleagues may expect you to have the same availability for extra projects as you did before baby. And your boss may continue to overload you with projects that you don't know how to say no to.

If you're struggling with setting boundaries at work, here are some sample scripts you can use, depending on the person with whom you need to set the boundary. Remember that you can set reasonable boundaries at work that protect your well-being while still being a great employee.

SCRIPTS TO SET BOUNDARIES AT WORK

With your boss:

"Thank you for asking me to help on the project. I am currently at full capacity right now. However, when I am done with _____, I will be able to work on it."

"It's important that I help out on this, I hear that. Right now, I don't have the capacity. If there are other ways I can help out, please let me know. Thank you for respecting that."

With your colleagues:

"Can you check this over for me?"

"Can you sign up for this committee? We don't have any other volunteers."

"Thank you for considering me, but I don't have enough time to commit to the committee right now."

"It is unfortunate that the committee cannot run without enough volunteers. I am still not able to help out."

With yourself:

"I have the ability to say no. Saying no to more than I can take on is taking care of myself. Overworking myself is not helping myself, my job, or my family."

Part of setting boundaries also involves figuring out the division of labor when it comes to your partner or spouse. The workload may need to change in the household when both of you are working. For example, perhaps your partner can be in charge of daycare drop-off while you shoulder the responsibility of afternoon pickup. Maybe you'll trade off doing the bedtime routine while the other person cooks dinner. Also consider how you'll divvy up the household chores that come with raising a tiny human. Perhaps you've been in charge of folding laundry, cleaning dishes, washing baby bottles, changing diapers, grocery shopping, and keeping the house organized. When you return to work, it's simply not feasible for all of this to continue to fall on you. Determine the extent to which you can divide and conquer in a way that feels equitable to you and your partner, and then maintain these boundaries as best you can. By brainstorming how you can share the workload of parenting, you can help ease the transition later. To read more on boundaries, check out chapter 3 for an in-depth dive into how to best set—and keep—your boundaries when it comes to motherhood.

For single parents, figuring out the division of labor can look different, especially when you don't have a supportive co-parent who can help you offset some of this load. (And as we said earlier, if you're a single mom, you are a true warrior.) If you need help juggling the balancing act of returning to work, make sure to reach out to your support system during this adjustment period, whether it's a friend, family member, or neighbor you can rely on. For example, is there someone who can serve as an emergency back-up for picking up your child? A neighbor who can watch your child for a few hours if you're running late at work? A family member who can help out on sick days? Identify who can be there for you when you need it. Remember that it's not realistic for you to balance it all.

If there is truly no support system you can lean on, then ask yourself whether you can create one by looking at resources within your community. Are there any community groups you can get involved in that will allow you to develop these supportive connections? If the answer is no, then it is important to learn what you can let go of today. What is on your to-do list that can wait until tomorrow and what are the things that you must do now? For example, cooking dinner is something you need to get done to feed your family, but it might be okay to leave the dishes or the vacuuming until the morning, or even later the next day.

RETURN-TO-WORK COPING PLAN

As you settle into your role as a working mom, know that it will take time for you and your family to adjust. During this time, make sure to check in on your expectations. Are you holding yourself to unrealistic standards? Are you expecting too much of yourself too soon? It's important to make sure you aren't stretching yourself too thin and neglecting your own needs. This is a recipe for burnout, which will leave you feeling emotionally disconnected, physically drained, and unable to function effectively in your multiple roles. Make sure to look over your warning signs for burnout, which we covered in chapter 8, so you can watch out for these symptoms before they cause you to completely crash.

However, know that regardless of any plan that you put into place, your journey back into the workforce might not go as smoothly as you hope. Prepare for there to be some hiccups! If you're having a hard day when it seems like nothing is going right—and those days will likely happen—know that you aren't doing anything wrong. Take it one day at a time and remind yourself that this is a huge transition for you. Use the following exercise to create a plan for returning to work after baby.

Exercise
Return-to-Work Coping Plan

Returning to work can be overwhelming—emotionally and physically—as you add the extra duties of parenthood to your to-do list. Fill out the following return-to-work coping plan to help you feel a little more prepared for your identity as a working mom. We've provided a sample plan for you first, followed by a blank template for you to fill in.

Initial concerns about returning to work:

> Feeling confident at work again
>
> Setting boundaries (i.e., being able to leave work at work)
>
> Balancing daycare drop-off and pickup

Positives of returning to work:

> Talking with other like-minded adults
>
> Having more financial stability
>
> Using a different part of my brain other than "mommy brain"

Boundaries I will set at work:

> Finding three times per day I can pump breastmilk
>
> Leaving work by 4 p.m. every day
>
> Limiting travel to once a month or less

How my partner and I will divide the household labor:

> We'll alternate dinner every other night
>
> I'll do bath time
>
> He'll do story time

Other people who can support me (and how):

> My mom (can be an alternate pickup person at daycare)
>
> My friend Darla (can watch the baby twice a month)
>
> My sister (can help with childcare on sick days)

My typical warning signs of burnout:

> Easy to anger
>
> Resentment
>
> Exhaustion

My typical coping strategies:

> Going for a walk
>
> Listen to music
>
> Reaching out to my best friend

Return-to-Work Coping Plan

Initial concerns about returning to work:

_____

_____

_____

_____

Positives of returning to work:

_____

_____

_____

_____

Boundaries I will set at work:

_____

_____

_____

_____

_____

How my partner and I will divide the household labor:

_____

_____

_____

_____

Other people who can support me (and how):

_____

_____

_____

_____

My typical warning signs of burnout:

_____

_____

_____

_____

My typical coping strategies:

_____

_____

_____

TAKEAWAYS

It is not easy to return to work after having a baby. It is a time that's filled with a variety of emotions. While you may be excited to experience some adult interaction again and look forward to fostering another part of your identity outside motherhood, you may also simultaneously feel grief and loss at the prospect of missing out on parts of your child's life. Whether you are on one end of the spectrum or somewhere in the middle, we want you to know that you aren't alone in these feelings. Being a working mom is no easy feat. We hope you had a chance to reflect on some of the challenges that come with returning to work and that you took away a couple of tools to help you prepare.

18 Baby Sleep (and Your Own Sleep Deprivation)

Sleep has become an obsession on social media. Whether it's Instagram, Facebook, or TikTok, everyone is talking about baby sleep, mom sleep, or the lack of both. Did you know that the infant sleep industry is a multimillion-dollar industry? There is so much information swirling around out there when it comes to getting your baby to sleep (and dealing with your own sleep deprivation) that it can be overwhelming. And nothing brings out the mommy shamers more than seeing others put out information that they don't agree with. If you want to see passionate arguments unfold on social media, just mention "how are you helping the baby sleep" (or give *any* opinion about baby sleep) and buckle up for a wild ride.

This chapter is here to provide you with the evidence—the sound science—that has been proven regarding infant sleep. We want to give you the facts. That's it. Although we'll also share our own sleep stories and adventures, we want you to do what works for you, your baby, and your family. Sleep train, don't sleep train, co-sleep, don't co-sleep—do whatever you feel is best. There is no one right way. We want to empower you to make the decision that is best for your family and your values.

One word of advice: Find a few online sleep accounts that fit with your values. We know moms who decided to sleep train for their mental health, and moms who decided not to do any kind of sleep training at all. All of these moms are good moms.

SAFE SLEEP GUIDELINES

Before diving into sleep specifics, we absolutely want to discuss what safe sleep is. The following guidelines on safe sleep apply to infants up to one year in age (American Academy of Pediatrics):

SAFE SLEEP GUIDELINES

- Put babies to sleep on their backs (not their stomachs or sides).
- Room-share but don't bed-share.
- Keep soft objects and loose bedding away from the infant's sleep area.
- Don't use drugs or alcohol.
- Avoid commercial devices that are inconsistent with safe sleep recommendations.
- Make sure there are no pillows, blankets, or other items that could cause overheating.
- Use a firm sleep surface.
- Consider offering a pacifier at bedtime and naptime.

We always advocate for safe sleep. Although the above guidelines advise against bed-sharing, we want to acknowledge that bed-sharing is incredibly common in various cultures around the world, and there are safe ways to do so. Of course, we want moms to be educated on the fact that there are risks associated with bed-sharing—and *oh my*, was there ever controversy on one of our social media posts that discussed the importance of supporting moms in their decision on how get their baby and themselves sleep—but at the end of the day, we want moms to be supported. No one knowingly puts their baby in danger, but there are desperate moms out there struggling with sleep deprivation. At the end of the day, we want moms to be empowered and knowledgeable when it comes to their baby's sleep. With that in mind, let us share both of our sleep stories.

OUR SLEEP STORIES

Caitlin

When I got pregnant, I would frequently hear comments like "Sleep while you can" or "You will never sleep well again once the baby comes," but I really didn't think too much of it. I had done shift work and worked night shifts for years, so I was used to broken sleep—just getting a couple of hours here and there. Well, let me tell you, PPA and sleep deprivation are a nasty combination. The sleep deprivation was hard. So hard. Nothing really prepares you.

After my son was born, I was incredibly anxious and couldn't sleep well when he was actually sleeping (and whenever I finally did fall asleep, he would wake up again). There were weeks where I ran on two hours of sleep a night. It was out of control. I prioritized getting things done around the house instead of resting when he was sleeping, and to top it all off, I had purchased a video monitor with a sensor pad that went off if it detected no movement within 30 seconds. Let's just say that it did not help my anxiety when it went off whenever my son slid too far down in the crib. When he was nine months old, he was still waking up pretty consistently twice a night, and I was getting increasingly anxious about how I'd return to work since he was often difficult to settle back to sleep. How was I going to see five clients a day for therapy?

So how did I do it? I sleep trained my baby. There, I said it. This was before the "no cry-it-out" movement took hold on social media, so I didn't worry about what kind of backlash I would receive if other people knew I sleep trained my baby. (And that whole movement sounds a little misleading anyway—don't all babies cry?) But to be perfectly transparent, if I had known about other methods, I likely would have explored those first. At the time, though, I didn't have the resources to hire a 1:1 sleep coach, and I just did what I felt I needed to do to be okay.

Chelsea

My kiddo was a terrible sleeper. I don't even know how long it was until he slept through the night. (Spoiler: He does now…usually.) To be quite honest, I knew very little about babies' sleep and didn't have the capacity to research it after navigating NICU life. I was 100 percent winging it. Whether that was right or not, I am not sure. Would I have sleep trained or looked for sleep resources had we not been through the NICU experience? Probably. However, I just didn't have the emotional capacity to learn one more thing. It still felt like I was in survival mode, and I didn't even think about learning more about sleep options.

Reflecting back on our experience, some sleep education would have probably been helpful in alleviating some of the intrusive thoughts I was having. Without the NICU monitors at home, I sometimes had intrusive thoughts of him not breathing at night, so I would constantly go in and check on him. I also had no baby monitor, as I was trying my best to break away from any type of observation. (Spoiler #2: When he was 16 months, I got a baby monitor. It made checking on him so much easier.) I don't think I can accurately articulate my experience because everything is such a blur. When it comes to sleep, all I remember is being so tired that I didn't know how I was going to get through some days and wondering if I would ever sleep again. It sounds dramatic, but when you are the thick of it, it can really feel like it will never end.

WHAT EXACTLY *IS* SLEEP TRAINING?

Sleep training—sometimes called sleep coaching, teaching, or learning—involves helping your baby learn how to fall asleep and stay asleep on their own. It also involves teaching them to how to soothe themselves back to sleep when they inevitably wake up in the middle of the night. There are many different types of sleep training methods out there that, when used consistently, can help your baby begin sleeping on their own within days.

There are many benefits to sleep training, the most obvious one being that everyone gets more rest, which is important for baby and parents alike. However, we want to advocate that you should do what is best for *your* family. If that involves sleep training, great! If it doesn't, that's perfectly okay too! You are not harming your child either way, and the research shows this. We also want to acknowledge that in many cultures around the world, sleep training is not the norm. When we asked our Instagram community about their experience with sleep training, we found that it was common among parents in the United States, Canada, the United Kingdom, and Australia, but it was not common among those in Europe, South America, or Africa.

Misconceptions about sleep training abound, so let's break down some of these myths right now:

- **Myth:** If you sleep train, you are leaving your child to cry it out for hours on end.

    Fact: Your baby will cry if you sleep train, but this doesn't mean you are leaving them to cry by themselves all night. The most widely cited methods don't involve you shutting the door and leaving your baby until the morning.

- **Myth:** Once you sleep train, your child will sleep well forever.

    Fact: As with anything else, there will be periods of regression. Sleep training does not guarantee that your child will sleep through the night all the time. Occasional regressions are to be expected and do not mean you have done sleep training "wrong."

- **Myth:** You can sleep train a two-month-old.

    Fact: You cannot sleep train babies until they are four to six months old. Prior to this age, they have not yet developed the capacity to self-soothe, nor are their circadian rhythms mature enough for sleep training methods to be effective. However, you can promote good sleep hygiene through having a solid bedtime routine.

- **Myth:** If you sleep train, you cannot comfort, rock, or hold your child.

    Fact: If you want to rock, comfort, or hold your child, then you can absolutely do so. Make it part of your routine and incorporate it into whatever method of sleep learning you're using.

- **Myth:** If you sleep train your child, you are ruining their sense of secure attachment with you.

  Fact: There are countless children who have been sleep trained who have a strong, close, and loving relationship with their parents. Attachment is built through a continual series of actions in which a caregiver is responsive to a baby's needs. This can involve feeding the baby, changing their diaper, and comforting their cries with a soothing touch. Secure attachment is about being a consistent caregiver to your child, and sleep training does not interfere with this.

- **Myth**: If your baby is tired enough, they will sleep.

  Fact: The reality is that babies usually need help from us to fall asleep, and the more tired they become, the more difficult it can be to get them to sleep. (Anyone who has dealt with an overtired child can attest to this.)

DECIDING WHAT'S RIGHT FOR YOU

There's a lot of parenting advice out there when it comes to getting your baby to sleep, with over 60 percent of parenting books endorsing sleep training, 30 percent opposing it, and roughly 10 percent taking no position altogether. It can be incredibly frustrating to keep up with the information overload. When we polled our online community, here is what some parents found to be helpful versus unhelpful in deciding what was right for them.

HELPFUL

- Taking shifts with my partner
- Being aware of the baby's awake windows and the signs of a tired baby
- Learning about normal infant and toddler sleep and adjusting expectations
- Sticking to a schedule
- Not looking at the clock
- Going for a walk
- Letting go of expectations
- Learning about sleep norms across cultures
- Reading about safe bed-sharing
- Reading safe sleep resources backed by evidence
- Having a partner who helped make decisions when I felt like I was too tired
- Eating family meals

NOT HELPFUL

- Hearing everyone's opinions
- Reading too much information
- Trying to get my baby to fit into a sleep consultant's rule book
- Following social media accounts that made me feel guilty or upset for my sleep training decision
- Hearing other people say, "Sleep when the baby sleeps"
- Using a sleep tracking app
- Feeling the constant societal pressure to sleep train
- Dealing with people telling me to stop breastfeeding because it would help my baby sleep

The bottom line is *you are not a bad mom if you choose to sleep train, and you are not a bad mom if you choose to co-sleep.* If any sleep-related resources make you feel guilty or shameful about your choices, move on. While it is completely okay for resources out there to provide alternatives, it is not okay to make moms feel bad for their choices or make them feel like they are ruining their child. Find sleep resources you trust and that empower you.

BEDTIME ROUTINE AND BABY SLEEP

Although it's completely up to you whether sleep training is right for your family, two areas in which you absolutely cannot go wrong are having a good bedtime routine and educating yourself about baby sleep. For many parents, these two factors alone can reduce the need to implement additional sleep interventions.

A bedtime routine is important because it helps babies figure out the difference between daytime naps and bedtime sleep, which can really help them get in those longer stretches of sleep at night. A calming and soothing bedtime routine also helps babies become familiar and comfortable in their sleep environment. Routines mean predictability, and predictability means safety and security! For all these reasons, we are firm believers in a good sleep routine. Some parents like a longer routine, while some like a shorter one. Either way, do what works for you. Here is an example of a routine we did with our littles when they were babies:

- Bath time
- Massage (some babies love this)
- Pajamas

- Milk before bed (bottle or breast)
- Story time
- In crib (with a song in the crib and a kiss goodnight)

In addition to helping you develop a solid bedtime routine, we wanted to provide education on some common baby sleep questions that can give you a better understanding of what to expect when it comes to baby sleep:

- **"When will my baby sleep through the night?"** While many parents might be hoping that their newborn baby sleeps through the night after the first few weeks, the reality is that 37 percent of infants don't sleep longer than six consecutive hours when they are 6 months old, and almost 30 percent still don't at 1 year old (Pennestri et al., 2018). Therefore, if your baby is 7 months old and still not sleeping through the night, know that this is normal. It's not as if your baby will hit six months of age and then magically start sleeping. We wish someone had told us this when we first had kids!

- **"Why does my baby take the shortest naps?"** Unfortunately, it is developmentally normal for short naps to occur until your baby is around five to six months age, as they are not yet mature enough to connect their sleep cycles together. However, here are some other reasons your baby may be having short naps: it is too light in the room, they are overtired or not tired enough, or they weren't put to bed full enough (causing them to wake up from hunger).

- **"What is the best sleep training method out there?"** On social media, you can find every type of sleep training expert, coach, and consultant under the sun, and often their advice can be contradictory. Some claim that sleeping training is harmful, while others say the exact opposite. The bottom line is that there is no one-size-fits-all approach (for babies or for parents) when it comes to sleep training. Therefore, it's important to take into consideration *your* family values and what is important for your baby and for you as a parent. Find one or two online accounts that resonate with your values and unfollow all the rest.

- **"Will a sleep diary actually help?"** Yes, it can! A sleep diary can allow you to see patterns of sleep-wake association that you wouldn't have noticed otherwise. One great book is *Secrets of the Baby Whisperer* by Tracy Hogg and Melinda Blau (2011), which discusses what to document when your baby sleeps, including the length of time they sleep, what you and your baby were doing before sleep, and their sleep behaviors.

COMBATTING SLEEP DEPRIVATION

It probably doesn't come as a surprise that sleep deprivation has been found to negatively affect our mental well-being and make us more prone to aggression, rage, and irritability. (Caitlin can certainly attest to this. During her bout of baby-related sleep deprivation, her fuse was short and her reactivity was cranked up to a 10. Suffice it to say, she was not the kind of mom, wife, or friend that she wanted to be.)

When we are sleep deprived, the vast majority of us get downright cranky. We don't need much research to find that this is true. However, sleep deprivation can also worsen the effects of depression, anxiety, and other related mood disorders, which is why creating a plan to combat sleep deprivation is so essential. As a new mother, it's not always possible to avoid sleep deprivation altogether—it's an unfortunate reality that comes with the territory of having a new baby—but there are ways to mitigate its effect on your mental health. Here are some recommendations for getting the most of your sleep.

1. **Take your sleep seriously.** Although you probably have an endless number of tasks crowding your to-do list, you need to prioritize your sleep as best as you can. That means your seemingly never-ending pile of laundry can wait if you can sneak in another 30 minutes of sleep. Although it's tempting to stay up late under the guise of productivity, there will *always* be things that need to get done, and the reality is that you're not being particularly productive anyway when you're running on fumes. Make sleep one of your top priorities.

2. **Practice a bedtime ritual.** Bedtime rituals aren't just for kids, so explore what makes your bedtime space cozy and comforting. Use essential oils, lotions, or whatever makes you feel soothed. For Caitlin, it's a bath, a good book, and a weighted blanket.

3. **Aim for quality over quantity.** You're likely not going to be getting extended periods of interrupted of sleep with an infant in the house, so prioritize quality over quantity. A few hours of rested sleep are better than six hours of broken sleep. If you have a partner, ask them

to take turns getting up with the baby so you can get a three- or four-hour stretch of sleep in. If this isn't realistic, then aim for two hours between feeds.

4. **Refresh yourself.** Although sleep is certainly the best way to recharge your body, it's not the only way. Do one thing each day that refreshes you, whether it's having a cup of coffee, going outside, or washing your face with nice cleanser. It is important to still have a piece of the day that you find enjoyable, or at the very least, refreshes your mind and body.

5. **Shift your thoughts.** It seems simple, but just shifting your mindset can make a big difference in your mood. That's because our thoughts, feelings, and behaviors are all interconnected, so changing how you think can create a ripple effect in how you feel and behave. See what it's like to say, "This is hard, but I can make it through today" rather than "I am never going to be able to get through the day."

6. **Avoid late-afternoon caffeine.** We know, we know. How can we ask you to give up that afternoon cup of coffee when you're running on empty to begin with? Rest assured, we're not telling you to avoid caffeine altogether. But drinking caffeine after 2 or 3 p.m. can wreak havoc on your sleep and leave you wide awake when it's time for bed, worsening the effects of sleep deprivation.

7. **Ask for help.** There's no sense in trying to power through sleep deprivation on your own. If you're able to, enlist the help of a family member, partner, or member of your support system to let you take a power nap during the day. Find ways to share nighttime duties, such

as splitting the night shift. If you're nursing, find other ways that your partner can help, such as taking over that late-night diaper change or giving a bottle of pre-pumped breastmilk. Even if you're a single mom, ask for help! See what close friends or family members can drop in for the occasional overnight shift. You might be surprised who is willing to help.

Use the following exercises to help you put some of these steps into practice.

Exercise
Affirmations for Sleep Deprivation

Here are a few affirmations that we recommend for when you're feeling exhausted or drained after a few (or many!) sleepless nights. Please take what works for you, leave what doesn't, and adapt any of the statements to fit your own experience better.

This is a hard moment.

I can ask my support system for help. I deserve rest.

This is a tough season.

I will be okay and my baby will be okay if we don't sleep tonight.

I will take moments of rest tonight.

I will close my eyes when I can and let go of the need to be productive.

Exercise
My Sleep Plan

If you're wondering whether you *really* need a plan in order to sleep, the answer is yes, you do. We are advocates of being prepared for all things. Preparation is the key to life when you have kids. A sleep plan can prepare you for the multiple night awakenings and give you strategies when you are too exhausted to think. Refer back to this sleep plan often during those tough nights.

If I have a hard night with lots of interruptions, here are some steps I can take to recharge myself the next day (e.g., take a one-hour power nap, take a hot shower, put on a facial mask):

_____

_____

_____

_____

If I'm struggling with thoughts that I'll never sleep again, here is what I can tell myself instead (e.g., "This won't last forever," "This is hard, but I can get through it"):

_____

_____

_____

_____

These are the support people I can rely on if I need to sleep:

_____

_____

_____

_____

These support people can help me during the day in the following ways:

_____

_____

_____

_____

These support people can help me at night in the following ways:

_____

_____

_____

_____

TAKEAWAYS

Figuring out how the heck to get your child to sleep is one monumental task in motherhood. Although everyone will have different opinions on what they think is the "correct" way to get your baby (and yourself) to sleep, it's okay to disagree. It's okay to have different values when it comes to sleep. We want you to do what is right for *you*. Remember that you are the best mom for your baby, no matter how you decide to tackle the issue of sleep.

19 Social Support

When you enter the world of parenthood, you'll hear all sorts of messages about the importance of social support: Make sure to find your village, make sure that you have a "mom squad," make sure that you don't go through the transition to motherhood alone—the list goes on and on. Heck, we've said similar things throughout this book! While social support *is* so incredibly important, you might be wondering what kind of supports other moms have. You might not know where to even find support.

When we asked our online community about their experiences with social support, we were blown away by how much of a pain point this area is for so many parents. We knew it was a source of struggle for many, but we had no clue just how many moms felt like they were drowning when it came to friendships and motherhood. Here is just a snapshot of some of the struggles they shared:

- "I am at a completely different stage of life than my friends."
- "I feel so disconnected from non-parent life."
- "I don't know what to talk about with my friends."
- "My non-parent friends can't understand why I can't do shit without planning."
- "Friends without kids don't understand that I'm not always available."

- "I'm losing childless friends who don't grasp how mentally and physically occupied I am now."
- "My friend is trying to conceive, and after my baby was born, we stopped talking."

These struggles have been amplified in the era of COVID-19, which has made it even more difficult for new moms to stay connected. It's been challenging to adapt to a world where Mommy and Me groups, prenatal hospital classes, and playdates aren't always conducted face-to-face. As you're reading this book, we're not sure what society will look like. Maybe Zoom meetups will be the new norm, or maybe COVID will be a distant memory (fingers crossed). Regardless, there are so many expectations and beliefs around the concept of social support that we felt the need to dedicate a whole chapter to the topic. Our goal is to give you information, resources, strategies, and a sense that you are not alone in this. We'll start by sharing our own experiences.

OUR FRIENDSHIP EXPERIENCES POSTPARTUM

Caitlin

During my childless years, it was easy to maintain a sense of social support. I could go out for lunch, dinner, and drinks whenever, and sleep in as late as I wanted on the weekends. Going on a spontaneous weekend getaway was a breeze. I was also very close to many of my coworkers due to the nature of working rotating shifts, which involved odd hours and tough cases.

I was the first among my close friend group to have a baby. During my pregnancy, I was experiencing a lot of relationship stress due to the breakdown of my marriage, and many of my friends supported me during this process. They gave me the most beautiful baby shower and were a constant support of consolation with phone calls and visits. Of course, I had some friends who said they would visit but never did.

After the baby was born, I struggled to find fellow mom friends due to the extreme nature of my PPA. While I did meet two moms through a Mommy Connections group—whom I'm happy to say I became good friends with and still talk to today—I never ventured out much further than these two friendships. I felt anxiety all the time. Whether it was going to the library or attending a Mommy and Me class, I questioned myself constantly. Would someone judge me? Was I being too friendly (or not friendly enough)? Did I have my "resting bitch face" on? (And how could I turn it off?) It was exhausting going out and making conversation when I spent the whole time wondering whether I was saying the right thing. Replaying it in my head now, I realize how silly it sounds, but at the time I was deep in the throes of PPA.

After my daughter was born several years later, it became increasingly evident that the friends who disappeared after my first was born were never coming back. Although I could have reached out, the time and distance that had passed made it harder to connect. I concluded that if they didn't want to make the effort to reach out to me, then I was finished with the friendship. I didn't have PPA this time around, so I tried to expand my social circle by attending a few Mommy and Me classes. I met a group of moms whom I felt I could connect with on a more personal level, but the classes ended shortly after the COVID pandemic began, which really put a hold on growing any of these friendships closer. We attempted to stay in contact through a Facebook group, but nearly two years later, updates from that group are few and far between.

Since that time, I have continued to stay connected with my small group of close friends, but my friend group has not expanded. My husband and I recently moved into a new neighborhood with several families with young children, and our hope is to nurture these relationships for both ourselves and our children.

Chelsea

As with Caitlin, I was much more of a social person in my childless years. I had many girlfriends I could reach out to and meet up with whenever I needed my social fix. Because getting together didn't take a lot of mental energy or planning, friendships just felt easy at the time.

I was in the middle of the pack when it came to getting pregnant. Luckily, I had a few seasoned mama friends ahead of me and a few childless friends behind me. At the time, I honestly didn't think much about how having a baby would impact my friendships. I was more excited that three of my closest friends and I were all pregnant at the same time. This led to a lot of dreaming of what our postpartum period would like together.

However, my world was rocked when I had a premature baby. The experience was extremely isolating since my husband and I had to move over two hours away to be with our son while he was in the NICU. I also felt alone and misunderstood, like I couldn't relate to other moms with what seemed to be "normal" birth experiences. Of course, people checked in on us and offered to do anything they could, but when you are in that type of situation, I think several different things happen. First, you don't know how to describe your experience or know what you even need. Second, you are living in such a survival mode that it's difficult relate to others. Third, when you are away from home that long, people's lives continue to move forward while you get stuck in a place where time feels like it stands still.

During our NICU stay, I found comfort in the other families who lived at Ronald McDonald House and was able to form a true community with them. I don't think I would have managed as well as I did without them.

Although our friendships have changed since returning home, there are a few I keep in touch with and whom I hold dear to my heart.

Once the three-and-half month isolation in the hospital was over, the COVID pandemic hit and I was once again alone—but this time, so was everyone else. I know they say misery loves company, but the loneliness and isolation I had just experienced I did not wish upon anyone. Yet it became a reality. Still, I am so lucky to have a few girlfriends whom I've kept in touch with all along. We do our best to check in on each other whenever we can, whether it's through texts, phone calls, or sometimes video conferencing. While this circle of friends is small, they've helped bring me out of dark places, even though they probably don't know it.

YOU'VE GOT A FRIEND IN ME. DO I HAVE A FRIEND IN YOU?

When you're looking for social support, it can be helpful to know what you want and expect from your friends. That's because what is considered social support looks different for every person. What one person classifies as supportive may be too "in your face" for another person. A brief "How are you doing?" text may be just the right amount of support for another. What we all have in common is the need to feel seen, heard, and like we matter.

Exercise
What Do I Want in a Friend?

What we look for in a friend can change over the years, especially after we have children. However, we all want friends who treat us how we would like to be treated. Use these questions to reflect on the types of friendships you would like to have.

What types of friends are you drawn to?

_____

_____

_____

_____

_____

What qualities do you value in a friendship?

_____

_____

_____

_____

_____

What are your expectations in a friendship?

_____

_____

_____

_____

_____

What makes you feel heard and valued?

_____

_____

_____

_____

_____

How do you let someone know what you need?

_____

_____

_____

_____

_____

THE COMMON FRIENDSHIP CONCERNS OF MOTHERHOOD

Even when we think we know what we want in a friend—as well as what we are *not* looking for in a friend—there are some common barriers that can get in the way. Let's unpack some of the common concerns we heard from parents regarding friendship and motherhood:

1. **We are in different stages of life.** Changing jobs, relocating across the country, having babies, getting married, focusing on your career—these are some of the things that can lead even the closest of friends to drift apart. We received hundreds of messages when we asked our online followers about the hardest part of friendship and motherhood. The dominant answers were: *We drifted apart. We don't have that much in common anymore. It's harder to find things to talk about.* We get it—when babies come into the picture and you're trying to juggle your work and home lives, the first things to go out the window are the text messages with friends and the long back-and-forth chats. If this sounds like you, let's explore some strategies to reconnect with friends when you are in different stages of life:

    -   **Remember why you became friends in the first place.** Reminisce about old memories, funny stories, or past experiences. When you remember all the times that you shared together—the good, the bad, the funny, and the embarrassing—it can bring you a sense of nostalgia. This can facilitate closeness even if your life today looks vastly different than it did when you used to spend more time together.

    -   **Carve out time.** Set aside a time each week to message your friend and check in on each other's successes and struggles.

Being vulnerable and authentic creates a sense of closeness that's often lost through superficial connections.

- **Be upfront and assertive.** Be sure to let your friend know what is realistic for you in this season of your life. Whenever you find yourself responding to potential plans with "Maybe" or "I'll get back to you," know that your answer is most likely going to be a no. Be upfront about this. Keep in perspective about what is reasonable for you when it comes to your time, your finances, and so on.

- **Avoid making assumptions.** When we would socialize with many of our childless friends, we tended to keep kid talk to a minimum because we (incorrectly) assumed they didn't want to hear about it. Then our friends started asking us questions like "Tell us more about the kids! What are they loving? What are they wearing? What are their friends like?" If you aren't sure how much to talk about a certain topic, check in instead of making assumptions. You might be surprised.

- **Avoid the comparison trap.** Although it is human nature to compare, it can take away from a friendship if you're always minimizing the good things and amplifying the bad things that are happening in your life. Even if it seems like your friend has this magical life compared to you, remember that you don't know always what is going on behind closed doors, even when it comes to our close friends.

At the end of the day, though, know that some friendships simply dissolve with time. Some that drift apart may never regain a sense of closeness. It can be hard to accept that friendships change and evolve. It's okay to feel the many emotions that come up with all the changes and movements happening in your life. Give yourself permission to feel that sadness and let go of any guilt.

2. **Making friends as an adult is hard.** We've heard from so many of you who have said, "How do I even make friends as an adult? I feel so awkward finding mom friends! It's so much harder to make friends than it was at other times in my life." If only it were as easy as playing with the same toy and all of a sudden—*besties!* Developing friendships in adulthood can certainly be challenging because, let's be honest, it's not as easy as it was in elementary school. (Though sometimes it wasn't easy then either.) If you're looking to make new friends, here are some tips to help you when you meet others:

- **Ask open-ended questions.** When you meet a potential mom friend, ask questions to show that you actually care about the other person and are interested in what they have to say. This is a beautiful way to spark a conversation and listen to the other person's thoughts, feelings, and opinions. You'll find that most people love to share when given the chance. And it can be flattering when someone shows curiosity in them.

- **Then ask follow-up questions!** You want to show that you have heard the other person and are interested in what they have to say. When you're focusing on what the other person has to say, it makes it easier to stay present and not get caught up in worries about how you're coming across.

- **Don't take over the conversation.** Be aware of how long you are talking, pause, and make it reciprocal. The general rule of thumb is to not talk for over 30 seconds—otherwise, the person tends to drift off.

- **Take a risk when meeting someone new.** Often, you can be so afraid of rejection that you don't put yourself out there enough. See what it's like to be vulnerable and take a risk. For example: "I enjoyed our chat today. Would you want to meet up for a coffee or take a walk on the weekend?" You may surprise yourself by making the first move. And if the person turns you down, remember that it's not necessarily about you. You don't know what is going on for other people behind the scenes.

- **Find common interests.** We have bonded with friends over our love of country music, curling, and true crime shows. Some of our closest friendships are simply grounded in our similar sense of humor. We can laugh at the same things, watch the same silly videos, and react to situations in similar and amusing ways. Highlight what is similar between the two of you.

- **Offer support.** Offer to be a small part of someone's support system, even if it's just for a few minutes. You never know what could come of it! Caitlin remembers going to a rhyme-time class at the library and seeing a mom of twins who was struggling to get both children out the door. Caitlin offered to help put the boots on one twin, while the mom grabbed the other twin who kept running for the hills. Fast-forward, they ended up exchanging numbers and planning a play date. Small gestures of kindness can go a long way, and sometimes all it takes is one small act to make a mom's day better.

Overall, you want to develop friendships with people with whom you feel safe and can be your authentic self. No façades, no masks. And the number of friends doesn't really matter. Although we're sure you can think of someone who always has birthday parties with 50 people, or that bachelorette who goes on vacation with 30 of her closest friends, quality is more important than quantity.

THE PEANUT APP: TINDER FOR MOMS?

Several years ago, when we had our first kids, we had a conversation that there needed to be an app like Tinder for making mom friends. Fast-forward a few years later and *ta-da*, there is! It's called Peanut, and you connect with other mothers by swiping up on profiles that seem to have similar interests as you (or swiping down if you want to move along). Once you find a match, you can start chatting. Peanut can be so helpful in building friendships since it's often easier to talk to someone new over social media, and it eliminates some of the barriers that go with meeting friends the old-fashioned way.

3. **I don't know where to find my village.** So many moms have asked us about how to find their village: "Where is my village? Is it bad if I don't have a village? Is my child going to miss out?" Everyone talks about the importance of having a village for their child to grow up with, but it's important to recognize that not every person's village will look like a scene from *Modern Family*. Not all parents have friends and family who live close to them, and not all parents are even close with their family. If the thought of building your village seems overwhelming—maybe you are starting over in a new community, have moved across the country, or have found that

your village is not there for you in the way you want or need—here are some tips to get you started:

- **Finding your village while pregnant.** Explore prenatal classes available in your area by checking with your community hospital, local doulas, or yoga studios. There has been more attention given to moms' prenatal health in recent years, so there are many more resources out there now dedicated specifically to pregnant moms.

- **Finding your village with a newborn.** Look into infant classes at your local health center. After Caitlin had her second child, she took a class called Baby Steps, which is partially funded by our health care system. Within this class, a number of moms decided to sign up for another Mommy and Me class that connected mothers of babies under 12 months as well as toddlers.

- **Finding your village with a new baby and toddler.** This is one we have definitely found to be the trickiest! There are a variety of baby classes out there, some of which allow toddlers to join and some of which don't. Look in your community for local music groups, baby and toddler play classes, and children's museums. Hitting up a local playground is always a good bet too.

Ultimately, your village can consist of whoever is there for you when you need someone to lean on. This can include the Starbucks barista, your child's teacher, daycare workers, your doctor, or your therapist. It doesn't always have to include a picture-perfect family consisting of siblings, parents, cousins, and neighbors. Who is there for you? Who lifts you up? Who do you look at and think, *It's going to be okay*? That's your village.

4. **Social media makes motherhood feel like a competition.** Social media can be an incredible form of support, but it's also turned motherhood into a competition of sorts. Although it can be fulfilling to connect and see what other parents are doing, it also can fuel a fire in which you compare yourself to others and feed into self-deprecating thoughts at such a vulnerable time in your life. Not only that, but there's also a dark side to social media that can be used as a tool to target and bully others. We've had tons of trolls, rude comments, and bullies that have come after us on social media, and we have seen this with other parenting accounts as well. Most of the comments were passive aggressive, while some were downright rude, but what stood out to us the most were the number of "likes" these hurtful and mean comments had received.

So if you're on social media (and chances are, most of you are), we want you to be incredibly mindful of what you are consuming. Here are some tips that might help you navigate this process:

- **Set a time limit for your social media consumption each day.** When that time is up, put your phone away! When setting boundaries like this for ourselves, we purposefully leave our phones upstairs. This makes it harder to access our phones and results in less temptation to use them.

- **Follow accounts that are aligned with your values.** Each season, go through your page and do an account purge. Unfollow any accounts that irritate you or don't bring you joy. Unfollow that friend from high school you haven't talked to in 15 years or the former coworker who still complains about everything under the sun. Think of it as spring cleaning for your social media account.

- **"Kill 'em" with kindness.** If you find yourself around others who are constantly "one-upping" you, the best strategy you can implement is to give them support. We know this sounds counterintuitive, but we have found that this type of behavior typically comes from a place of insecurity. By validating the other person's positive attributes and strengths, it can lessen the competitive behavior. It can also facilitate empathy and compassion.

- **Set boundaries around some topics.** If there is one thing we have seen since beginning our Instagram account, it is that certain topics—namely, baby sleep, screen time, and breastfeeding versus formula feeding—can bring out the claws and cause people to say things that they later regret. We'll admit that we have both fallen into the trap of arguing with trolls when they criticize our posts, and it really is pointless to argue with someone over a screen. If you find that things tend to heat up around a certain topic, it may be best to leave it off social media and keep those conversations for in-person discussions.

At the end of the day, you want to engage with and follow people who uplift you, help you feel connected, inspire you, make you laugh, give you sound information, and help you feel seen and validated. If the accounts you follow don't meet these needs, give yourself permission to hit the "unfollow" button.

5. **I have no time to connect with friends.** When you become a parent, it can be hard to find the time to connect with friends. Other responsibilities take precedent, and you often don't have the energy, time, or ability to spend time with them (or at least definitely not in the same way). For example, we used to have friends over for dinner often, but after having babies, this is a quarterly occasion. On one recent occasion, Chelsea and her husband had some colleagues over for dinner, and it was a nice evening. After they left, her husband said, "That was fun, we need to have them over again." Chelsea's first thought was *No, that was exhausting*—it wasn't that the dinner was horrible, but she didn't necessarily value spending time with these people. They were nice people, but not the type of people she wanted to foster a friendship with.

    As you have less time, you need to prioritize the friendships that are worth your time and attention. These are the relationships that fill your bucket. These are the people with whom you can be your real and authentic self. Once you narrow down those friendships to those that you truly value, here are some tips to help you stay connected:

    - **Make it a point to do little things together.** Make plans, even if it's just grabbing a cup of coffee for 15 minutes in between errands. One of the biggest factors in maintaining friendships is the frequency of your interactions, even if they're brief. Ask them how their job is going or what they are doing for their holidays.

    - **Stay in touch.** Especially for long-distance friendships, make it a point to touch base twice a year if you're able to.

- **Start a group chat.** Have a dedicated space to chat with some of your close friends. Caitlin is currently in a few different group chats, and although everyone is at a different stage of their life and some live in different countries, people make a point to touch base in the group chat about once a month. Even if it involves reminiscing about a crazy time at work or sharing a funny meme, those brief connections can be just what someone needs in their day.

- **Support your friends' endeavors.** Sharing information about their small business online or like their photos. This lets them know that you're still thinking of them and that you care.

6. **It feels like my friendships are one-sided.** Healthy friendships are reciprocal, meaning that each person gives and takes equally in the relationship. Although there may be life circumstances that can cause these dynamics to temporarily shift—causing one person to be giving more to the relationship than the other—this should not be a continuous thing. Think of a friend you keep showing up for. Are you always the one reaching out? Are you always filling up their cup but not getting the same treatment in return? Or does it go back and forth? To help you determine whether your relationship is one-sided, here some friendship red flags to look out for:

   - **They don't respect you.** For example, they might put you down in public, constantly one-up you, or share your secrets with other people.

   - **They don't respect your time.** They're constantly canceling on you or changing plans at the last minute.

- **They're always in charge of making plans.** You get little or no say in the matter.

- **You're usually the one to call or text first.** (And whenever they do reach out first, it's often because they need something, not necessarily because they just want to hang out.)

- **It's always about them.** They dump all of their problems on you but don't offer a listening ear in return, making you feel like you need to keep your thoughts and feelings hidden.

- **They drain your energy.** You feel emotionally and or physically exhausted after spending time with them.

If these red flags are present, it's time to reevaluate your friendship with that person. The relationship doesn't necessarily need to end, but these red flags are signals that something needs to change. Communication is key here. Talk to your friend about your concerns. You might find that they've just been withdrawing because they are going through a stressful time. But other times, you might come to realize that they're just plain selfish, in which case it might be time to say goodbye.

7. **All my friends don't have kids yet (or their kids are much older).** When you're the first one in your friend group to have kids, it can be incredibly isolating to see friends drop off either quickly or slowly. It can also be difficult to see your friends transform and gain new friends as their identity shifts, which can make you feel left behind. This can happen for friends on both sides of the coin: friends with children who make new mom friends *and* childless friends who go on to expand their social circle with other friends who may be more

available. If you are struggling with identity shifts in any of your friendships, here are some tips:

- **Allow yourself to acknowledge that your friendship has evolved while still giving value to this relationship.** You can feel saddened by this relational shift while still making the friendship a priority. This will help keep your relationship intact, even if it looks different now.

- **Explore what you can do with the time that you have available.** Smaller, more frequent check-ins may be more realistic for you. Focus on quality, not quantity, when it comes to spending time together.

- **Remember who you were before kids came along.** Reflect on your shared memories, stories, and experiences. This may involve laughing about the ridiculous trends you thought were cool in high school or reminiscing on how you used to think people who were 40 were *so old*.

- **Set limits and boundaries when it comes to making plans.** Some activities may simply not be feasible for you as a parent. We once had a group of friends ask us to take a four-day trip, but as the parents of young kids, this was just not doable. Be upfront about your limits. The majority of people will take this well.

It can be hard when relationships evolve across time, with some becoming closer and some becoming more distant. But as long as you still place value in these relationships, you can still make time to find joy with those you love.

8. **My friend is trying to conceive and I feel guilty about my pregnancy and birth story.** How do you show up for your friends who are experiencing infertility or pregnancy loss? You want them to share in your joy, but you also don't want to make them feel angry, hurt, or resentful. When we consulted with friendship expert Miriam Mayer about this tough topic, here are some suggestions she had:

- **Show up.** One of the biggest sources of hurt and resentment that someone can experience is when no one shows up for them. Even if you don't know what to say, the simple act of showing up demonstrates that you care and that you don't want them to go through it alone.

- **Don't be afraid to talk about their struggle.** Allow your friend the space to grieve their experience. If they don't want to talk about it, they won't.

- **Keep them included.** Don't leave them off the invitation list when it comes to your baby shower or your kid's birthday party. Although this can be such a tricky situation to navigate—after all, you don't want to make it seem like you're rubbing it in their face—not inviting them can further their pain. Just because your friend is experiencing pregnancy struggles doesn't mean they can't celebrate your happiness. However, make sure to offer the invitation with a disclaimer that you completely understand if they aren't up to it. This gives your friend an easy "out" without making them feel excluded.

- **Don't try to make them feel better with unwelcome platitudes.** Offering your friend sayings like "Everything happens for a reason," "Things will all work out, it will be fine," "Just relax, it'll happen when you're less stressed" or "At least you'll have more time and money without kids" can only further their stress about trying to conceive. This is incredibly invalidating of their experience because you don't know what the future holds. This forced positivity can also make them feel alone in their experience.

TAKEAWAYS

Having friends who support and uplift you is crucial as you navigate the wild journey of motherhood. Explore what can you do together to connect, even if it involves running errands and getting some practical things crossed off your to-do list. It can be as simple as asking, "Do you want to come with me while I go shopping for new furniture?" or "Do you want to come with me to the gym?" In addition, don't underestimate the power of smaller check-ins and shorter conversations in helping you maintain a felt sense of security and closeness in your relationships. With the right friendships, you don't need to go through it alone.

Our
Goodbye

We were approached by our publisher, PESI, in March of 2021, who pitched us the idea of creating a postpartum mental health workbook. They had fallen in love with our Instagram account and appreciated how we dove in deep on the tough topics of motherhood—the stuff that others often shied away from. Although we had been researching and talking about maternal mental health for quite some time—we knew our stuff, we had the training, and we had the experiences—impostor syndrome quickly kicked in. *Umm you want us to write a book? Us? Two toddler moms?* After a lot of conversations and tons of support from our friends, colleagues, and families, we got to work.

What a wild ride. Many tears were shed writing this book. It took a lot of deep thoughts, exploration, discussion, and processing of our own experiences. Long nights spent at the computer after the kids were put to bed, researching and getting our trusted audience the sound information they need to make informed decisions.

In this book, you have learned about everything from breastfeeding to birth trauma to boundary setting. We have shared about our experiences—our own tough stuff—and we have given you the strategies and tools to help you manage your own emotions and experiences. We hope you continue to turn to this book whenever you feel unsure, anxious, angry, or exhausted. We hope it finds a comfy spot on your nightstand, your coffee table, or even your bathroom—wherever you can find a quick moment of quiet.

We know this book will be a starting point for many to learn about postpartum mental health, and we hope you gain the strategies you need and the validation that you deserve. That every parent deserves. You've got this. We are always here for you.

References

Allen, K. R., Blieszner, R., & Roberto, K. A. (2011). Perspectives on extended family and fictive kin in the later years: Strategies and meanings of kin reinterpretation. *Journal of Family Issues, 32*(9), 1156–1177. https://doi.org/10.1177/0192513X11404335

American Academy of Pediatrics. Infant sleep safety overview. AAP. https://www.aap.org/en/patient-care/safe-sleep/

Bardos, J., Hercz, D., Friedenthal, J., Missmer, S. A., & Williams, Z. (2015). A national survey on public perceptions of miscarriage. *Obstetrics and Gynecology, 125*(6), 1313–1320. https://doi.org/10.1097/AOG.0000000000000859

Berginck, V., Burgerhout, K. M., Koorengevel, K. M., Kamperman, A. M., Hoogendijk, W. J., Lambregtse-van den Berg, M. P., & Kushner, S. A. (2015). Treatment of psychosis and mania in the postpartum period. *American Journal of Psychiatry, 172*(2), 115–123. https://doi.org/10.1176/appi.ajp.2014.13121652

Bhat, A., Cerimele, J. M., & Byatt, N. (2018). Pregnant and postpartum women with bipolar disorder: Taking the care to where they are. *Psychiatric Services (Washington, D.C.), 69*(12), 1207–1209. https://doi.org/10.1176/appi.ps.201800133

Brown, B. (2006). Shame resilience theory: A grounded theory study on women and shame. *Families in Society, 87*(1), 43–52. https://doi.org/10.1606/1044-3894.3483

Buchanan, T. A., Xiang, A., Kjos, S. L., & Watanabe, R. (2007). What is gestational diabetes? *Diabetes care, 30*(Suppl 2), S105–S111. https://doi.org/10.2337/dc07-s201

Buchanan, T. A., Xiang, A. H., & Page, K. A. (2012). Gestational diabetes mellitus: Risks and management during and after pregnancy. *Nature Reviews Endocrinology, 8*(11), 639–649. https://doi.org/10.1038/nrendo.2012.96

Canadian Institute for Health Information. (2021). *Hospitalization and childbirth, 1995–1996 to 2019–2020 — supplementary statistics.* https://view.officeapps.live.com/op/view.aspx?src=https%3A%2F%2Fwww.cihi.ca%2Fsites%2Fdefault%2Ffiles%2Fdocument%2Fhospital-childbirth-1995-2019-supplementary-data-tables-en.xlsx&wdOrigin=BROWSELINK

Caplan, P. (2000). *The new don't blame mother: Mending the mother-daughter relationship.* Routledge.

Carberg, J., & Langdon, K. (2019). Postpartum obsessive compulsive disorder (OCD). *Postpartum Depression.* https://www.postpartumdepression.org/postpartum-depression/types/ocd/

Centers for Disease Control and Prevention (CDC). (2022). What is infertility? *CDC.* https://www.cdc.gov/reproductivehealth/features/what-is-infertility

Chapman, G. (2010). *The 5 love languages: The secret to love that lasts.* Northfield Publishing.

Ciciolla, L., & Luthar, S. S. (2019). Invisible household labor and ramifications for adjustment: Mothers as captains of households. *Sex Roles, 81*(7–8), 467–486. https://doi.org/10.1007/s11199-018-1001-x

Collardeau, F., Corbyn, B., Abramowitz, J., Janssen, P. A., Woody, S., & Fairbrother, N. (2019). Maternal unwanted and intrusive thoughts of infant-related harm, obsessive-compulsive disorder and depression in the perinatal period: study protocol. *BMC Psychiatry, 19*(1), 94. https://doi.org/10.1186/s12888-019-2067-x

Colino, S., & Fabian-Weber, N. (2021). Postpartum anxiety: The other baby blues we need to talk about. *Parents*. https://www.parents.com/parenting/moms/healthy-mom/the-other-postpartum-problem-anxiety

Devault, M. (1994). *Feeding the family: The social organization of caring as gendered work*. University of Chicago Press.

English, F. A., Kenny, L. C., & McCarthy, F. P. (2015). Risk factors and effective management of preeclampsia. *Integrated Blood Pressure Control, 8*, 7–12. https://doi.org/10.2147/IBPC.S50641

Heise, A. M., & Wiessinger, D. (2011). Dysphoric milk ejection reflex: A case report. *International Breastfeeding Journal, 6*(1). https://doi.org/10.1186/1746-4358-6-6

Hogg, T., & Blau, M. (2011). *The baby whisperer solves all your problems (by teaching you how to ask the right questions)*. Atria Books.

Ghaedrahmati, M., Kazemi, A., Kheirabadi, G., Ebrahimi, A., & Bahrami, M. (2017). Postpartum depression risk factors: A narrative review. *Journal of Education and Health Promotion, 6*, 60. https://doi.org/10.4103/jehp.jehp_9_16

Grekin, R., & O'Hara, M. W. (2014). Prevalence and risk factors of postpartum posttraumatic stress disorder: A meta-analysis. *Clinical psychology Review, 34*(5), 389–401. https://doi.org/10.1016/j.cpr.2014.05.003

Johnson, S. M. (2019). *Attachment theory in practice: Emotionally focused therapy (EFT) with individuals, couples, and families*. The Guilford Press.

Kersting, A., & Wagner, B. (2012). Complicated grief after perinatal loss. *Dialogues in Clinical Neuroscience, 14*(2), 187–194. https://doi.org/10.31887/DCNS.2012.14.2/akersting

Livingston, G., & Thomas, D. (2019, December 16). Among 41 countries, only U.S. lacks paid parental leave. *Pew Research Center.* https://www.pewresearch.org/fact-tank/2019/12/16/u-s-lacks-mandated-paid-parental-leave/

March of Dimes. (2021). *2021 March of Dimes report card.* https://www.marchofdimes.org/reportcard

March of Dimes Perinatal Data Center. (2011). Special care nursery admissions. *National Perinatal Information System/Quality Analytic Services.* https://www.kff.org/wp-content/uploads/sites/2/2013/01/nicu_summary_final.pdf

McBride, H. L., & Kwee, J. L. (2017). Sex after baby: Women's sexual function in the postpartum period. *Current Sexual Health Reports, 9*(3), 142–149. https://doi.org/10.1007/s11930-017-0116-3

Neff, K. D. (2009). The role of self-compassion in development: A healthier way to relate to oneself. *Human development, 52*(4), 211–214. https://doi.org/10.1159/000215071

Pennestri, M. H., Laganière, C., Bouvette-Turcot, A. A., Pokhvisneva, I., Steiner, M., Meaney, M. J., Gaudreau, H., & Mavan Research Team. (2018). Uninterrupted infant sleep, development, and maternal mood. *Pediatrics, 142*(6), Article e20174330. https://doi.org/10.1542/peds.2017-4330

Pope, C. J., Verinder S., & Mazmanian, D. (2014). Bipolar disorder in the postpartum period: Management strategies and future directions. *Women's Health 10*(4), 359–371. https://doi.org/10.2217/WHE.14.33

Raphael, D. (1975). *Being female: Reproduction, power, and change.* De Gruyter Mouton.

Rowlandson, N. L. (2010). *In/visible families: exploring the experiences of lesbian, gay, bisexual, queer, trans-identified, and two-spirited parents in Northern Ontario school communities* [Master of Education, Lakehead University]. http://knowledgecommons.lakeheadu.ca/handle/2453/3947

Sacks, A. (2018, May). *A new way to think about the transition to motherhood.* TED Residency. https://www.ted.com/talks/alexandra_sacks_a_new_way_to_think_about_the_transition_to_motherhood?language=en

Rizzo, K. M., Schiffrin, H. H., & Liss, M. (2013). Insight into the parenthood paradox: Mental health outcomes of intensive mothering. *Journal of Child and Family Studies, 22*(5), 614–620. https://doi.org/10.1007/s10826-012-9615-z

Scobie, O. (2020). *Impossible parenting: Creating a new culture of mental health for parents.* Dundurn.

Sit, D., Rothschild, A. J., & Wisner, K. L. (2006). A review of postpartum psychosis. *Journal of Women's Health, 15*(4), 352–368. https://doi.org/10.1089/jwh.2006.15.352

Stotzer, R. L., Herman, J. L., & Hasenbush, A. (2014). Transgender parenting: A review of existing research. *The Williams Institute.* https://williamsinstitute.law.ucla.edu/wp-content/uploads/Trans-Parenting-Review-Oct-2014.pdf

Tawwab, N. G. (2021). *Set boundaries, find peace: A guide to reclaiming yourself.* Penguin Random House.

Valdimarsdóttir, U., Hultman, C. M., Harlow, B., Cnattingius, S., & Sparén, P. (2009). Psychotic illness in first-time mothers with no previous psychiatric hospitalizations: A population-based study. *PLoS Medicine, 6*(2), 194–201, Article e1000013. https://doi.org/10.1371/journal.pmed.1000013

Webster, B. (2021). *Discovering the inner mother: A guide to healing the mother wound and claiming your personal power*. William Morrow.

Wilt, J. (2011). Normal families facing unique challenges: The psychosocial functioning of multiracial couples, parents and children. *The New School Psychology Bulletin, 9*(1), 34–41.

Winnicott, D. (1953). Transitional objects and transitional phenomena; A study of the first not-me possession. *International Journal of Psychoanalysis, 34*(2), 89–97.

World Health Organization. (2018, February 19). Preterm birth. *WHO*. https://www.who.int/news-room/fact-sheets/detail/preterm-birth

Yate, Z. M. (2017). A qualitative study on negative emotions triggered by breastfeeding; Describing the phenomenon of breastfeeding/nursing aversion and agitation in breastfeeding mothers. *Iranian Journal of Nursing and Midwifery Research, 22*(6), 449–454. https://doi.org/10.4103/ijnmr. IJNMR_235_16